# SECURITY BREACH

## THE MURDER OF TOD McQUAID

BY

JANET BAILEY McQUAID

Pittsburgh, PA

ISBN 1-58501-047-2

Trade Paperback

First Printing — 2004
Library of Congress #2002116927

Request for information should be addressed to:

SterlingHouse Publisher, Inc.
7436 Washington Avenue
Pittsburgh, PA 15218
www.sterlinghousepublisher.com

CeShore is an imprint of SterlingHouse Publisher, Inc.

SterlingHouse Publisher, Inc. is a company
of the CyntoMedia Corporation.

Book Design: Kathleen M. Gall
Cover Design: Jaime L. Jaczesko—SterlingHouse Publisher, Inc.
Photographs provided by Janet Bailey McQuaid



Printed in Canada

# DEDICATION

**Liz and Heather,** you were so young when your daddy's life was taken. I hope this book will help with any thoughts you have held inside. Always remember, your daddy loved you very much. He would be so proud of your accomplishments and the beautiful young women you have grown up to be. Keep him in your heart, and remember his "Star" will always be there for you.

**Rog,** we went through some really rough times. I thank God for answering my prayers and guiding us.

**Jeff,** you are my gift from God. I love you.

**Rose,** it has been a blessing having you with us.

**Bob and Jan,** thank you for your love and support during the trials.

**Sharon,** there aren't enough words to thank you. I am forever grateful.

My thanks and gratitude to Cindy Sterling and Megan Davidson. Writing this book was not an easy task for me. With your patience, and guidance, you have helped to make my dream come true.

**IN LOVING MEMORY OF**

Tod Edwin McQuaid
Harriet A. and Tod E. Bailey
Edwin H. McQuaid

# PROLOGUE

A TRUE STORY ... I wish to God that it weren't.

# LETTER TO DADDY

Dear Daddy,

I really really miss you. I love you so much. I wish I could have warned you that you had something in your drink then you wouldn't have drunk it and you would still be alive. You have missed so much. I broke both my arms when I was in the 2nd grade trying to jump off the high bar at gymnastics. I had a tutor come to the house to teach me. The last week of school in the 5th grade I ended up with appendicitis. I had a high score on the C.A.T.s at school and got an award signed by Bill Clinton, the president. Mom wishes she could have told you that she loved you before you died.

My friend Alissa and I were playing Ghost Writer. How come you didn't come down? I wish I could see you again even if you came as a ghost. I know you probably won't but if you do read this letter please write back somehow or come down and talk to me. Please.

Love your daughter
Elizabeth
Age 11

# CHAPTER ONE

I always thought there would be some sort of sign, a warning of impending danger, a bird stealing its way into the house, a picture falling off the wall. I thought people were supposed to have some sort of a sign. A couple of days before my father died, my mother got her sign. For several nights there was a knock at the door leading from her basement. It would awaken her from her sleep, and she would always answer the knock of the phantom visitor.

The only warning I got that my son Tod was in serious danger was a phone call from Tammy Wilson, the woman Tod had hired to work at his alarm and security business. I met her shortly after Tod hired her. He brought her to New York for a trade show, and we met for dinner at our favorite restaurant. I had suggested to Tod that I make dinner, but he declined. This was a subtle clue to me that he wasn't that interested in their relationship. It was strictly employer-employee.

My husband Rog and I arrived early at the restaurant. It was crowded with people chattering over the loud music. The hostess escorted us to a table, and we ordered a glass of wine while we waited for Tod's arrival. We discussed how proud we were of Tod's growing security business, TEMAC. We had originally thought Tod was taking a big risk when he sold his security business in Springfield, New Jersey, and started fresh in Lewisburg, West Virginia, a city that had one of the nation's lowest crime rates. Not a good place, we thought, for a business that depended upon people's need for security. Tod believed in himself and, as always, made things work. More importantly, he was happy.

"There's Tod," I said waving my red napkin in the air. "Doesn't he look handsome without that awful beard?" As was his habit, he had shaved off his beard for the summer. I watched with pride as he walked toward us. He was neatly dressed in a navy blue suit, white shirt, vest, and tie. He flashed a radiant smile when he saw us, and his blue eyes twinkled. I looked at the girl beside him, expecting someone tiny and petite, and was surprised to see that she was a husky girl of about five foot six or seven. She wore heavy, dark blue eye shadow with contrasting white up to her eyebrows, like a teenager experimenting with makeup. Her eyelashes were caked with mascara and her lips were bright red. Her clothes, in keeping with her taste in makeup, were overstated. A red top, several sizes too small, partially exposed her small breasts, and her skirt was so tight that it made her rounded hips look out of proportion to her body. Her heels made a loud, clopping noise as she walked toward us. She was talking softly to Tod, and I could tell from the expression on her face she wasn't happy. I continued to smile as I whispered to Rog, "Where did he find her?"

"Hi, Mom," Tod said, giving me a hug. He gently kissed my cheek.

Rog gave Tod the ritual hug. It was never too long or too close and always ended with a pat on the back. "This is Tammy Wilson," Tod said. "She works for TEMAC in the office."

"Welcome to New Jersey, Tammy." I extended my hand to her. Barely making contact, she shook my hand with her limp fingers.

"I thought it would be a good idea to bring her to the trade show to give her the chance to meet some of our alarm vendors and learn about the business," Tod said. "After all, she is going to be ordering equipment for TEMAC."

During dinner Tammy didn't talk much, and what she did say didn't tell me much about her. I didn't ask any of the typical questions I reserved for Tod's "lady friends" because I had the feeling that she was not going to play a major role in his life. I couldn't help but wonder why she seemed so unhappy, quietly listening while Tod caught us up on the latest news about his business. I tried to include Tammy in friendly conversation, asking her general questions. She answered me somewhat reluctantly, then reverted to her sullen expression. I had the impression she resented Tod for being with us, almost as if she were jealous of him. I felt that Tammy Wilson wasn't Tod's type. He was attracted to women who were friendly and fun-loving, and Tammy was proving to be neither.

When our waitress brought our dinners, I had lost interest in my food and barely tasted it. Something about Tammy Wilson bothered me, and I sat trying to figure out what it could be. "Do you want to stop by the trade show for a couple of hours?" Tod asked, taking a sip of wine to wash down his last bite of steak. Before I could decline, Rog said we would go. I reminded Rog that I had to baby sit our two grandchildren, Elizabeth and Heather. "You go." I said. "We'll meet up at the house later. The girls will be waiting for you, Tod, so don't be too late."

Elizabeth and Heather were Tod's two girls from his first marriage. Tod and Rose dated five years before marrying. Rog and I thought for sure they were a match made in heaven. We were sad when they separated and hoped they would patch up their problems, but after an extended separation they divorced. However, lately they seemed to be growing close again, spending more time together during his visits home. Elizabeth had said Tod had told her that he and Mommy might be getting back together. This thrilled us all.

I particularly loved Rose. She was a loving and caring person. Before the separation was final, Rog and I discussed with Tod the possibility of Rose and Elizabeth moving in with us. They came to live with us temporarily, but the arrangement worked out so well they never moved out. Rose became my daughter. She was company for me when Rog had to travel on company business, and having my little granddaughter close at hand was pure joy.

"I'll drop you off at the motel," Tod said to Tammy as he and Rog played tug-of war over the bill. Rog lost.

"You don't want me to go to the exhibit hall with you?" Tammy asked, sounding a little annoyed.

"No, I'd like to spend a little guy-time with my dad."

"Why don't you come back to the house with me, Tammy?" I offered.

"No, Mom," Tod said, nearly cutting off my words. "She'll be fine at the motel. Besides, there's some paperwork she needs to do."

"I'll do it later," Tammy said, taking her purse from the back of the chair. "I'll take you up on your offer, Mrs. McQuaid, if you don't mind."

I gave Tod a quick glance and could tell that he was a little upset. I wasn't sure whether he really wanted her to get some work done or if he did not want her involved that closely in his life. My guess was the latter.

On the drive back to the house Tammy remained quiet. I broke the silence by explaining the excitement that would occur as we entered the house. It didn't matter where we went or how long we were gone, Elizabeth and Heather always greeted us with hugs and kisses. True to form the girls greeted at the door. "Daddy, Nanny, Poppy!" They hollered. I hugged and kissed the excited girls as they glanced at the stranger standing in the foyer. Ignoring Tammy, Elizabeth grabbed Heather's hand and they ran to the front door. Not seeing Tod or Rog, Elizabeth turned to me. "Where's Daddy and Poppy?"

"Daddy had some business to take care of, and Poppy went along," I explained. "They'll be here in a little while." The girls turned away from the door and faced Tammy. Heather immediately hid behind me. I reached for her hand and wrapped my arms around her as I stood her in front of me. Elizabeth grabbed my skirt and clung close to my side.

"This is Tammy Wilson. She works in Daddy's office."

"Hello," the girls said quietly, in unison. Elizabeth looked at me with an expression that told me she was happy that the ordeal was over and asked if she and her sister could wait up for Daddy and Poppy.

"Only if Mom says okay, and you promise to be quiet so Tammy and I can visit."

The girls promised that they would be as quiet as mice. "Mommy's upstairs getting ready for her appointment," Elizabeth said as the two of them scurried up the stairs to get her approval. I knew it was only a matter of time before Rose came down the stairs. I began to feel tension building in my body. I had forewarned Rose about Tod bringing a female employee to the trade show. I didn't think Rose would feel threatened by Tammy but thought she might feel a little jealous. Perhaps Tod was right, Tammy should have gone back to the motel. It was too late to think about that now, so I had to make the best of it.

The girls returned with Mom's approval and proceeded to the end of the living room, where they had left their dolls. Tammy walked over to observe them as they began changing the clothes on their dolls. "What is your doll's name?" she asked Elizabeth.

Never taking her eyes off her doll, Elizabeth answered, "Jean Pierre."

"That's a nice name. Isn't that French?"

"Yes, Nanny brought him back from France for me."

Elizabeth was shy but never failed to give visitors a friendly smile. Her cool behavior now made it obvious that she didn't want to be bothered by Tammy. I couldn't understand what her problem might be, and suddenly it came to me. Tod had told Elizabeth that he and Rose might be getting back together again, and Tammy, in Elizabeth's eyes, posed a threat to that plan.

I heard Rose coming down the stairs and mentally began preparing myself for the introduction. Rose walked into the living room and made immediate eye contact with Tammy. "Hi, you must be Tammy. I'm Rose."

"She works for our daddy," Heather chimed in.

"Yes, I know" Rose said, smiling.

I sighed in relief as I watched Rose and Tammy give each other the once-over. Rose turned and rolled her eyes so only I could see her true feelings. "Excuse me, ladies, but I have an appointment with a client. I have all the necessary insurance papers ready for him to sign and should be finished in about an hour and a half," she said. "Nice meeting you, Tammy."

"You too," Tammy responded.

Rose hugged and kissed the girls, ordering them to behave as she left, closing the front door behind her. I was so relieved that the moment of introduction was over. My tense muscles began to unclench as I watched Tammy make her way to the sofa, sit down, and appear to relax. I sat down across from her on the antique love seat that Tammy was eyeing with great interest.

An awkward silence hung in the air as I searched my mind for something to talk to this woman about. Finally my manners resurfaced. "Would you care for something to drink?" I asked.

"Perhaps later. I can't get over how beautiful Tod's daughters are," she said, picking up a photo of the girls from the end table. "Tod's forever talking about them. They're the same age as my daughters."

"How many children do you have?" A sense of relief washed over me, knowing she was married.

"Two girls, and a little boy two-and-a-half," she sighed as a faraway look crossed over her face.

"How lucky you were to be able to get away," I offered. "Is your husband watching the children?" I was hoping she answered yes.

"No, I'm divorced. My mother has my little boy." She paused, a flash of anger glaring in her eyes. She explained that she was in a custody battle for her little girls because the court had awarded them to her ex-husband, and now she was fighting to get them back.

There was never a question between Tod and Rose where the children should remain. They put the girls first. It's always unfortunate when divorcing parents aren't able to work things out quietly for the sake of their children.

"Oh, Mrs. McQuaid," she blurted catching me off guard. "You don't know what I've been going through." Tears began to well up in her eyes. She searched her purse for a few seconds, than produced a tissue and carefully dabbed her eyes as she vowed to continue to fight until she got her girls back. I was surprised that her ex-husband had custody of her girls when the court usually favored the mother. I had a feeling there had to be a good reason why Tammy didn't have her children. Tammy surprised me further by telling me her ex-husband had an affair with a married woman who had his child. According to her, the mother didn't want the child and Tammy had adopted her. Because her ex-husband was the biological father of both girls, the court felt they should stay together and granted him custody.

"The woman gave you the rights to her child?" I asked incredulously.

"I know this doesn't make sense, but it's true," Tammy replied. "Those girls should be with me, and I'm going to keep fighting until I get them back," she vowed.

I was curious about her little boy. Why didn't her ex-husband have custody of him? The answer sounded like the plot of a soap opera, as Tammy explained that her son was born out of wedlock when she served one year in the army and his father was somewhere in California.

"The United States Army?" I had never heard of anyone serving one year in the armed services and thought this hard to believe. I found her position oddly intriguing but wondered if she was really telling me the truth "What exactly did you do in the army?" I probed.

"I was put into nursing but due to a bad back I was transferred into security," Tammy said. "I did so well there they transferred me into the FBI where I did undercover work."

My jaw dropped. "How could you do that in one year?" I was certain she could detect the sound of disbelief in my voice.

Completely unruffled, she replied, "Well, I did. I'm a hard worker."

"What did you do with your children?" I asked, continuing my interrogation.

"I hired someone to take care of them," she said sincerely, but I still had my doubts.

Elizabeth, who had sidled up next to one arm of the sofa, joined in the questioning. "Did you wear a uniform?"

Elizabeth was very astute, and I shouldn't have been surprised she was listening to our conversation. Tammy glanced over the arm of the sofa. "Oh, how cute. Yes, I did."

"I'm going to be a doctor when I grow up," Elizabeth offered.

Heather, not wanting to be left out, hurried over. "Me too," she chimed in.

"You sure are sweet girls," Tammy cooed. "I'd love you to meet my two girls."

Suddenly, Tammy tugged at her tight skirt to straighten it out and moved to the edge of the sofa. "I have a wonderful idea," she said, raising her voice and clasping her hands together. "Why don't you bring the girls to Lewisburg for Thanksgiving? I should have my girls back by then. I know it's three months away, but it's good to prepare ahead. I'm renting a house from my dad and have plenty of sleeping space."

I politely declined her offer, explaining that we had planned our own family gathering. It didn't matter what I had said, though; I could tell Tammy had her mind made up. "I'm sure we can work something out," she gushed enthusiastically. "I can't wait for Tod to return so we can make plans." She paused a moment, then bluntly asked, "Say, do you know if Rose still loves Tod?"

I was shocked to think she would ask such a question. My instant response would have been to say, "Yes," but I decided not to go down that road with her. "Tammy, that's a question I don't care to answer."

"Well then, do you know if Tod still loves Rose?" She was determined to get an answer one way or another.

"Whatever feeling Tod and Rose may have for each other is strictly between them, and personally, it's no one else's business. Not mine or yours."

"I'm asking because I love Tod very much."

Surprisingly her confession didn't startle me. I figured even if Tammy did love Tod, which I doubted, I was certain that Tod did not share that affection for her. He kept asking Rose to move back to West Virginia. I wasn't sure where Tammy's conversation was headed, but I knew that Elizabeth and Heather couldn't help listening. I suggested they go into the family room and play while I would put on one of their favorite movies.

Once the girls were settled, I returned to the living room where Tammy was waiting with more questions. "Don't you find it awkward having Rose and the girls living with you?"

I resented this stranger asking such rude questions. I tried to think of a subtle way to tell her that Tod and Rose still had feelings for each other, but I realized that an elephant didn't notice when you hit him with a fly swatter. "No, I don't. Tod wanted Rose to live with us. Rose is a gem, and the girls are delightful."

"How did Heather come about?" Tammy asked next.

I thought that that was a rather stupid question and began to laugh. "Tod and Rose spent a weekend together. They weren't divorced when Heather was born." I decided to hit the nail on the head and try to end this third degree. "Even after Tod and Rose divorced, he came home for weekends and they dated, if you want to call it that. Sometimes after a divorce, love is still there, and some couples continue a relationship. I've actually known couples that divorced and got along better afterward."

Tammy sat in silence with her eyes downcast. I thought she was mulling over what I had said. Suddenly, she raised her head and stared at me. "Say, did Tod tell you that the TEMAC office was robbed?" she said calmly.

Now she startled me. Tod hadn't mentioned this. "When did that take place?"

"Last month." Tammy claimed that Evelyn Gettman, a girl that Tod had dated, and her two brothers rammed knives in the kitchen walls, broke mirrors, stole money and some of Tod's jewelry, cut up Tod and Rose's wedding pictures, and, before leaving, ripped up the plants in his garden.

"Where was Tod when this took place?" I asked, not even trying to hide my concern.

"Doing a guard check," she replied casually.

I knew Tod would never leave his office without turning on his alarm system, so I was having a hard time believing Tammy and told her so.

"Tod had his alarm on, but Evelyn knew the code," she explained. "I even saw them leaving the house"

"That's funny, Tammy, because Tod changes his code from time to time."

This surprised her, and she paused for a moment. "Yes, I know he does," she continued, "but somehow Evelyn got the code. Another thing you should know," she continued. "Evelyn threatened to kill Tod. She said if she couldn't have Tod, no one would."

I wasn't sure how to react to her comment. I questioned her about the threat, thinking she might have misunderstood something.

"Oh, I'm not mistaken. I'm very sure," she said, nodding. She crossed her legs, letting her pantyhose line show. "He swore out a warrant for her arrest on the break-in, and, as usual, the Lewisburg police just ignored it. Every time Tod talked to them about it, they gave him a big runaround." Tammy leaned forward, and lowered her voice to a whisper. "Mrs. McQuaid, please don't tell Tod about this.

He'll be angry if he knew I told you. I know how you worry about your sons." She leaned against the back of the sofa and smiled.

I was upset. My son's life had been threatened and, strangely enough, I wasn't supposed to talk to him about it? Tammy said, still smiling, "I'm sorry I upset you. I just thought you should know."

Just then the front door opened and Rose appeared. The girls ran to greet her. "Mommy, Tammy wants to know if Daddy and you love each other," Heather said, giving her mother a hug. "You love Daddy, don't you?" Rose gave me an immediate frown followed by a puzzled look.

I quickly shook my head as a signal to ignore the question for the time being. Rose took my cue and she and girls went into the kitchen.

Curiosity was killing me, and I finally asked, "Tammy, how did you and Tod happen to meet?" She perked up and explained the event without hesitation. She had returned to West Virginia after being released from the Army and saw the TEMAC advertisement in the yellow pages. Since she was looking for a job she called them. Tod explained that he had two positions open, a security guard and operations manager. She felt qualified for both positions. After an interview, Tod hired her, and for two nights worked as a security guard, since the company was shorthanded. She then took over the position of operation's manager.

"You certainly are a Jack-of-all-trades, aren't you?" I said. "Being able to run an office, and everything else you've done, too."

"Sort of," she answered, sounding doubtful.

*Sort of* was a strange answer. Either she could run an office or she couldn't. "When did you say you started working for TEMAC?"

"The end of July."

"That's less than a month ago."

"Yes, but it seems longer than that."

As I listened to her, I tried to determine her ethnic heritage. She might be of Italian, Mexican, or even American Indian decent with her long, straight, black hair, brown eyes, and olive complexion. When we made eye contact, an eerie feeling washed over me. I saw nothing in her eyes but shadows and emptiness. She was different and strange, and I knew there was something very wrong about her.

The kitchen phone rang, and Rose quickly answered it. After a few minutes of conversation, I could hear her explaining that it was past the girls' bedtime. "You can say goodnight to them and see them in the morning. I'll see you when you get here."

Rose called out to me saying that Tod wanted to speak with me. I excused myself and went into our bedroom to take the call. Tod began by apologizing, saying they were going to be later than they anticipated. He asked if I would take Tammy back to the motel.

"Consider it done," I replied.

"And Mom, would you happen to have some homemade cookies and coffee ready when we get back?"

He knew, as well as Jeff, that when they came home, cookies were always waiting for them. We said good-bye, and I returned to the living room to give Tammy Tod's message.

She folded her arms and pouted. "Why doesn't he want me to wait here?" she whined.

"I really don't know."

The girls came in for their good-night hugs and avoided eye contact with Tammy. "Aren't you going to say goodnight to Tammy?" I asked. Together they yelled goodnight as they ran up the stairs. As Rose reached the bottom of the stairs, Tammy got up from the sofa, walked over to her and asked where the powder room was.

Rose glanced at me, then pointed down the hall to the powder room on the first floor. "Or you can use our bathroom at the top of the stairs to your right."

Tammy chose to go upstairs. Rose glanced back at me with a look of displeasure. I just raised my eyebrows in surprise and shrugged my shoulders. Rose got the girls settled into their rooms, then joined me in the kitchen where I was loading two little cereal bowls into the dishwasher. "Would you please tell me what's going on with that woman?" Rose asked. A look of annoyance marred her pretty face.

"Rose, your guess is as good as mine." Suddenly yells and laughter cascaded down from the second floor. "You'd best go check on Tammy and the girls," I said, as a feeling of panic filled me. Rose was a calm, soft-spoken person, but at that moment she was far from happy. She headed up the stairs as I stood at the bottom to listen.

Tammy was in Heather's room, and Elizabeth had joined them. Both girls were laughing so hard that my apprehension slipped away. I could hear Rose, angrily demand to know what was going on. I heard Elizabeth's footsteps as she scurried back to her room. Rose didn't wait for an explanation. "Tammy, you will have to excuse us."

"Rose, could I read them a story?" Tammy asked. "I love reading to my children, and with my girls living with their father, I miss not reading to them at night."

"No," Rose answered flatly. "Please go back downstairs."

Tammy complied. "I hope I didn't cause any problems by going upstairs," Tammy told me, trying to look apologetic, but I wasn't fooled. "The girls' rooms are lovely."

I got up from the love seat. "Tammy, it's rather late. I really should be getting you back to the motel." I handed Tammy her purse and walked her to the door. I had had enough of Tammy Wilson for one evening.

We drove off without another word. Tammy broke the silence after a few minutes. "Mrs. McQuaid, I didn't want to talk about this in front of the girls, but there is something else you should know. Tod's having some health problems."

"Tammy, to be perfectly honest, if Tod was having health problems, I think he would have told me. But when he comes home tonight I'll ask him how he's feeling, okay?" I kept my eyes on the road as I clenched the steering wheel. I was pretty sure that Tammy was lying. But why? She became flustered and begged me not to talk with Tod about it. I was tempted to stop the car and confront her; instead, I stepped on the gas pedal and roared into the parking lot like a teenager.

"I had a wonderful evening, and I can't wait to see you all again!" Tammy exclaimed. Then she put her finger close to her lips. "Remember to keep Tod's health a secret, okay? We don't want him upset." She shut the car door and waved good-bye.

On the drive home I tried to unravel all her stories. I pulled into our driveway to find Tod's red Bronco parked in the street. I entered the house and made my way to the kitchen where Rog, Tod, and Rose were seated around the kitchen table drinking coffee and munching on cookies.

"Hi, what's happening?" I asked.

Tod stood up and gave me a hug. I hugged him back. "I assume you got Tammy back to the motel okay?"

"Oh, yes," I answered with a sigh.

"So tell me, Mom, how did the evening go? What did you think about Tammy?"

I didn't answer. Instead I poured myself a cup of coffee, sat down at the table and stared at my son. "Tod, explaining tonight will take some doing. I'm not sure where Tammy is coming from, or what she is after." Tod looked at me in disbelief. "You know, she asked if you and Rose loved each other," I said, shaking my head.

Tod laughed. "What did you tell her?"

"There's nothing funny about that woman, Tod," Rose chided him.

"Do you really know anything about Tammy?" I asked him, and my questions tumbled out like water from a broken dam. "Where has she been? What's she's done? Do you believe all she tells you? Frankly, some of the things she talked about just don't add up."

"What are you saying, Mom?"

I told him about her claim of serving only one year in the Army, which seemed ridiculous to me. Tod shrugged, unimpressed. He said that he hadn't bothered to confirm it, and that it wasn't important. "And what kind of health problems are you keeping secret from me?" I asked.

Tod's eyes grew round as he stared at me in surprise. "What? What are you talking about? Do I look like I'm having health problems?" He stood up and puffed out his chest. "Fit as a fiddle. Where did you get such a wacky idea?"

"That's what Tammy told me."

"Why would she tell you something like that?" Tod was finally beginning to sound as annoyed as I was.

"Maybe you should ask her."

Rog, who had been sitting quietly all this time, got up from the table, walked to the refrigerator and made himself a ham sandwich. He was a typical engineer, taking his time, saying little, listening a lot. "I wasn't impressed with her," he said at last. "Those tight clothes and all that makeup."

"Did it ever occur to you to do one of your investigative profiles on Tammy before hiring her?" Rose asked as she placed her cup in the sink.

"No, I didn't," Tod said with a frown. "Her private life is none of my business and I don't want it to be my business. I'm too busy with TEMAC to get involved in other people's problems."

"Well, I hope she doesn't become your problem," I offered. Then I changed the subject to something we could all agree on. "The girls certainly are growing up quickly, aren't they?"

Everyone nodded, and we each had our own little story to tell about how smart, pretty and athletic those two girls were. I was so enchanted with the stories that I almost forgot about Tammy Wilson. Almost, but not quite.

# CHAPTER TWO

That evening, as I entered the bedroom, I found Rog already asleep. Trying to be as quiet as possible, I sat down at the little table by my bed and watched the twinkling stars. I thought about Tammy. I just didn't know what to make of her. I was about to climb into bed when I heard a soft knock on the door. It was Rose.

"Can we talk?" she whispered.

"Great idea. Let's go into the family room and have a glass of brandy." A few minutes later, Rose was relaxing on the sofa and I was curled up in Rog's reclining chair.

"What about Tammy?" Rose finally asked.

"I'm not sure. She's different from anyone I've ever met. I was shocked that Tod didn't do an investigative profile on Tammy, especially because he told me he does one on everyone that applies for a job. I think Tammy pulled the wool over Tod's eyes, and that's why he never bothered to do a security check on her."

"I wouldn't call it wool . . . ." Rose and I both laughed. Then suddenly she grew very serious. "What if Tod marries Tammy?"

The thought made me shiver. Tammy, my daughter-in-law. That just couldn't happen. "I have a feeling we have seen the last of Miss Tammy Wilson. Tod will see through her and she'll be history." Rose seemed relieved, and a bright smile returned to her face. The clock struck 1:30 A.M. as we headed off to bed. I fell right asleep without another thought of Tammy.

Six hours later, the sun was streaming into my eyes as I lay in bed. I wanted to roll over and ignore the morning, but the aroma of fresh coffee kept calling me. Finally I gave in, made my way to the kitchen, and found Rog loading the dishwasher. The girls were in the family room watching Saturday morning cartoons on the television.

"Quite a night, wasn't it?" he said, handing me a cup of coffee in my favorite mug, which had cheery yellow butterflies printed all around it.

"I don't think I could handle a discussion about it right now," I said, taking a sip. Just then I heard Tod holler, "Anyone home?" Before I had the chance to answer him, Elizabeth and Heather began yelling as they ran down the hall to meet him. He walked into the kitchen with both girls in his arms. The trade show had closed, and he had stopped to say good-bye before heading back to West Virginia. I wanted him to stay for lunch, but he declined. The girls begged him to stay as he sat down. He explained he had to get back to his business and promised to come back in a few weeks.

Heather gave her dad a kiss, then out of the blue asked, "Daddy, where is that funny lady?"

Tod hesitated. "She's waiting in the Bronco."

He glanced at me and I could tell from his expression that he did not want to discuss Tammy any further. I let the subject drop. I was happy to have had Tod home. His departure, however, always left us all crying. He wiped a tear from his eye. It broke his heart to leave his girls. He wrapped his arms around them and tenderly said, "Daddy loves you so much. When I come back, I'll bring the kittens, okay? I think those two miss you as much as you miss them. Now, promise me you'll be good girls for Mommy, Nanny, and Poppy."

Through their tears, Elizabeth and Heather kissed him and told him how much they loved him. "Remember, I love you, too," I said, handing him a bag of cookies. He gave me one of his beautiful smiles and looked at me for a moment. "And I love you, Mom." His eyes were filled with such tenderness, that I knew I would never forget that moment. Then he walked over to Rose and put his arms around her. It was an emotional time for him, and he had to glance down at the floor to compose himself. "I've got to get out of here before the traffic gets bad."

After he drove away, the two girls stood staring out the window, their gaze focused on the spot where his car had disappeared.

The following weeks were busy ones for me. I was in extra

rehearsals with my Sweet Adeline chorus in preparation for the upcoming international competition in Salt Lake City. My phone calls to Tod were few and far between. When he called I wasn't home, but fortunately he was able to talk with his girls.

It was mid-September and was I home alone. I finally had the chance to read the last chapter of my romance novel. Book in hand, I had no sooner nestled down on the family room sofa when the phone rang.

"Oh, hi, Mrs. McQuaid." It was Tammy Wilson. "Tod's going to be angry with me for calling you, so please don't tell him about this call. There's something I really think you should know."

I had heard those words before. "What might that be?" I asked impatiently.

"Late last night, when Tod was working on some new bids, he suddenly fell to the floor in pain. He had a heart attack. I didn't know what to do for him. I was so scared."

At first a shock wave moved through me, then I began to consider the source and calmed down a little. "Did you call 911?"

"No, Tod said not to. He said this had happened before and knew what to do. So when he was all right I went home."

Why would she leave him if he was having a heart attack? I asked myself. I didn't believe her. "Tammy, why are you only calling me now if this happened last night?"

"He told me not to call. He doesn't want to worry you."

"Where is Tod now?" I asked, my impatience growing by the second.

"Well, that's another thing," she said, very matter-of-fact. "Tod wanted to surprise you but I guess it's okay to tell you. Tod's back in college. He's taking evening classes. He's there now."

"Now, I find that interesting," I replied, making no attempt to hide my skepticism. I was certain that Tammy could detect the doubt in my voice, but I was wrong. She actually thought I believed her.

"Oh, Mrs. McQuaid, I can tell that you're upset about the heart attack. I just thought being his mother you have the right to know about his health."

"Thank you for calling, Tammy. Please have Tod call me when he gets in."

There was a moment's silence on the other end of the line as Tammy considered her answer. "After class he always goes out with the boys for a beer and doesn't get home until late," she said. "Besides, if you tell him we talked, he'll really be angry with me, so please don't tell him." she pleaded.

"Okay, I won't," I lied. "Just have him call me. I don't care how late it is." I hung up the phone in disbelief. I was convinced that this girl had nothing to do but make up wild stories about my son. It was implausible to think someone could have a heart attack one night and go out drinking with the boys the next. What was Tammy doing?

When Rog came home, I told him about Tammy's phone call. He shook his head. "It sounds like the fewer dealings we have with her the better," he said. I agreed, but I couldn't help feeling worried for Tod. I knew he didn't have a heart attack, but he was involved with a woman who was either desperate for attention or borderline crazy. When Tod didn't call, I tried to reach him, but no one answered the phone. Around 3:00 A.M. I gave up trying to contact him and went to sleep.

I woke up at 8:00 A.M. and called the TEMAC office first thing. Tod answered. "Honey, is everything all right?" I blurted, unable to hide my concern. "Are you sick?"

"Yeah, but it's only a head cold, no big deal," he said, sniffling a little. "How did you know I was sick?"

"Mother's intuition," I explained, deciding not to tell on Tammy just yet. "Now, what's this I hear about you going back to college?"

"How did you find that out? It was supposed to be a surprise. And don't tell me it's mother's intuition."

"A little bird told me," I joked. "Now, tell me about your classes."

"I'm taking Criminal Law 101," he said proudly. "I finally took the bull by the horns and decided it was time to get my degree. It's going to be a long haul running a business and taking night courses, but I can do it." His determination showed in his voice.

"Dad and I are so proud of you." I paused, choosing my next words carefully. "Tod, actually, the reason I called is that I'm concerned about your health. Tell me about the chest pains you've been having."

"What are you talking about, Mom? I have this lousy head cold that has settled in my chest, but that's it," he said, clearing his voice. "Where did you get the idea I was having chest pains?"

"From your operations manager."

"Tammy? Why would Tammy tell you something like that?" Tod sounded annoyed.

"Tod, I think that Tammy's unst ...." I stopped myself. Yes she was unstable but he probably wouldn't believe me anyway. "Listen Tod, please tell Tammy not to call me anymore, okay?"

Tod snorted into the phone. "Honestly, I don't know where she's coming from sometimes. I'll have a talk with her, Mom."

A couple of days passed. Tammy didn't call again, but I couldn't shake a strange feeling of discomfort whenever I thought of her. After a lovely stroll outdoors early one day, I called Tod to check up on him. "Good morning," I said, "I was looking at the beautiful autumn leaves today and it made me think of you."

Tod's cold was gone. He was excited about signing three new customers and hiring a new security guard, who would help him install alarms. I shared in his joy, knowing the long hours he had worked building his business. He had a dream and he was making it come true. Then the tone of his tone of voice changed to that of a little boy. "Mom?" he said. "Could you bake me some chocolate chip cookies with extra chocolate bits and mail them to me?"

How could I say no to my charming young man? "Of course, sweetie."

"Great, thanks. Don't know what I'd do without you. You're the best, Mom," he said, gleefully.

Elizabeth and Heather came in from the family room and wanted to talk to their daddy. I wasn't sure I would get a chance to talk with him before we left for Salt Lake City and said I would call him from there to let him know how our chorus had placed. After we said good-bye, I gave the receiver to Elizabeth. If I had known this would be the last time I would be able to speak with my son, I would have never gotten off the line.

On October 15, 1990, ten days after I last spoke with Tod on that beautiful autumn morning, a phone call from Tammy Wilson changed my life.

It was 5:00 P.M. and I was in the kitchen starting dinner. My dinner preparations came to a halt when the telephone rang. I answered, and she said hello. I was not expecting Tammy's call nor did I wish to speak with her. "What can I do for you?"

"Mrs. McQuaid, I'm calling to see if you've heard from Tod."

"Not recently," I answered.

"He didn't call to make arrangements about Thanksgiving. He promised me he would call and finalize the plans for you, Mr. McQuaid and the girls. I can't believe he didn't call," she said, angrily.

As far as I was concerned, the Thanksgiving conversation was a dead issue, though obviously, in her mind, it wasn't. "Tammy, you have no reason to be angry with Tod. Our Thanksgiving plans are made and we are not coming down to West Virginia. I hate to cut you short, but I'm ...."

"Mrs. McQuaid," Tammy interrupted me. "There is something you should know that may change your mind."

"And what could that possibly be?"

"Tod is buying me a ring for Christmas."

"I'll wait to hear that news from Tod." That ring was all in her mind, I thought. I didn't believe her for one second.

"And Mrs. McQuaid, Tod and my little boy had a blood test done and Tod is his father. So I guess you have a new grandchild."

I felt I couldn't let her get away with this whopper, so I called her on it. "Tammy, you and I both know that isn't true, don't we? You told me your son's father lives in California. And you just met Tod." I could hear my voice growing louder. "What are you trying to pull?"

Tammy ignored my question. "There is something else I think you should know. Tod's been gone for a week. He's called the office every day except the last two days, and I'm worried about him."

"What?" I hollered.

"Tod went out to serve a warrant. He always calls the office every day for his messages, but he hasn't called the last two days." There seemed to be real panic in her voice.

"Where did he go to serve the warrant?" If she was telling the truth, and I believed that she was, I had reason for concern.

"I don't know," she answered.

"What was the name on the warrant? Surely you know that."

"He wouldn't tell me."

"Tammy, you mean to tell me that you work in that office, and you don't know any of that information? How could you not know what is going on?"

"Well, I don't." I heard anger rising in her voice. "Tod doesn't tell me everything. There are things he doesn't want me to know."

I knew Tod wouldn't be gone that long without telling someone where he could be reached for emergency purposes, that just wasn't his nature. There was something wrong with the picture Tammy was painting, and I was losing my patience with her. "When did Tod say he would be returning to the office?" I demanded.

"He didn't. That's what has me worried. He should be back by now. I don't know what to do, Mrs. McQuaid."

I had had it with Tammy and her helplessness. *Wait a second*, I told myself, trying to calm down. This woman was up to something. She was trying to get back at me because I had ruined her Thanksgiving plans. "Tammy, I'm not sure I believe you." I knew Tod wouldn't trust anyone for any length of time to take charge of his business, especially not a new operations manager prone to making up wild stories.

"Mrs. McQuaid, it's true, believe me," she screamed. "I'm not lying. If I don't hear from Tod soon, I'm going to call the police."

Now that comment threw me for a loop. Was she serious, or was it a ploy to shake me up even more? I needed to sit down. I reached for a kitchen chair and pulled it toward me. "Tammy, let's go over this whole thing again. I want to make sure I know exactly what you're saying." After questioning her again, I decided that she was indeed lying and ended the conversation with the comment that Tod was probably enjoying the fresh mountain air and would be back in the office by the end of the day.

"I hope you're right, Mrs. McQuaid. I'm afraid something's happened to him."

Ignoring that comment, I asked her to have him call me when he returned. After we hung up, I tried calling Tod at the office, but there was no answer.

I went back to preparing dinner, but I couldn't shake the nagging feeling that there was something very wrong about Tammy's call. Why would she call to discuss Thanksgiving plans, then tell me she hadn't heard from Tod in two days? The more I thought about what she said, the more I began to imagine all sorts of frightening scenarios. What if something awful had happened to Tod? What if he had had an accident in the mountains and was unconscious? How would anyone know? How would we ever find him?

Minutes after Tammy's call, Rog, Rose, and the girls walked in. Rose immediately ushered the girls into the family room. Rog pitched in and began helping me with dinner. I felt his gaze on me as I moved about in the kitchen, keeping busy. "So tell me, what happened while I was gone?"

I walked over to the door way of the family room and listened as the girls talked about their day at school. Then I turned to Rog, struggling to hold back tears. "Tammy Wilson called."

Rose heard me and came into the kitchen. "What did Miss Tammy have to say?"

I hesitated. The more I thought about Tammy's phone call, the more I was beginning to have mixed feelings, not knowing just how to react to what she had said. "I need to discuss Tammy's call, and if the girls would play on their own for a little while, I'll put dinner on hold." Rog poured us each a glass of wine and we proceeded into the living room, leaving the girls in the family room to build a castle out of Lego blocks for their dolls.

Rog and Rose sat quietly and listened while I explained Tammy's conversation. "Do you think there's any truth in what she said?" I asked, rubbing my hands together.

"Remember the heart attack episode?" Rog asked. He stood up and began pacing the floor. "First of all, we know it's not unusual for Tod to serve warrants, and we all know Tod wouldn't trust anyone but himself with his business. On the other hand, it wouldn't surprise me if he decided to spend a night or two under the stars to relax and think." With this comforting thought he sat back down beside me.

"That's what I think, too," I said. "But why would she make up such a bizarre story?" I was starting to get a sinking feeling in my stomach.

"Remember, Tod's been hunting in the woods with Grandpa Bailey since he was twelve years old," Rose said. "He knows how to take care of himself."

Dinner was quiet except for the chatter and laughter of Elizabeth and Heather. I kept thinking of Tammy's phone call and tried to hide my concerns, to no avail. After dinner Rose took the girls upstairs to prepare their baths. I called Tod's number again but there was still no answer. I picked up the romance novel I had been reading when the phone rang. I ran into our bedroom to answer it. I was expecting to hear Tod's voice. Instead it was Tammy.

"Mrs. McQuaid, I heard from Tod."

"Thank God!" I felt a flood of relief wash over me. My son was alive and well after all. "He is all right then?"

"No, I don't think so," Tammy said very calmly. "He told me that he'd been shot and that he was behind a mountain in Meadow Bridge. He told me to get Carl, he'd know what to do. Then his radio phone went dead. I called the police but they don't believe me."

I began shaking like an aspen leaf in a high wind. I fired questions at her faster than she could answer. "What do you mean he's been shot? Where was he shot? Where is Meadow Bridge? Who's Carl? Why won't the police believe you?"

"I'm just telling you what Tod said." I could imagine Tammy shrugging her shoulders. "He said he was shot. As for the police, that's the way they are. Carl is the head guard. I called him, but he doesn't know anything."

"Who would want to shoot Tod?" I realized I was shouting but I couldn't stop myself.

"I don't know," Tammy said. "Do you remember me telling you about the girl that broke into the TEMAC office? Remember I told you she threatened to kill Tod? Well, she lives in Meadow Bridge, and it wouldn't surprise me if she or one of her brothers shot Tod."

I didn't really believe her, but I had nothing else to go on. "Tammy, you're not keeping something from me, are you?"

Suddenly her voice became clipped and abrupt. "Look, Mrs. McQuaid, I'm going to call the police again. I'll call you back as soon as I know something."

Before I had a chance to ask any more questions, she hung up. I sat on the bed stunned, holding the receiver so tightly that my fingers turned white. I called out to Rog and Rose, who came running.

"My God what's wrong?" Rose asked, sitting down beside me.

"It was Tammy on the phone," I said, putting my free hand across my mouth. I began sobbing. "She said that ... Tod's been shot!" My body was shivering and my hands felt like ice. I repeated my conversation with Tammy as best I could remember. "Why is she doing this? What kind of person would make up such a story?"

"Jan, calm down. I'll try to get to the bottom of this," Rog promised. "I don't understand why the police wouldn't believe Tammy."

"It sounds to me like she really went off the deep end on this one," Rose said.

"Let's not jump to any conclusions until we have more details," Rog reasoned.

"Our son's been shot behind a mountain somewhere, maybe bleeding to death. My heart's about to leap out of my body, and my body is shaking like crazy. And I'm freezing. And you're saying not to jump to conclusions!" I watched him wringing his hands as he paced around the floor in deep thought.

"I think Tammy Wilson is lying and Tod is fine," Rog said at last.

"I think Rog is right." Rose's voice trembled as her eyes filled with tears.

I began walking around the house not knowing what to do and found myself constantly checking the clock. Rose got the girls off to bed, and Rog went back to the computer. I was reading in our bedroom when the phone rang. It was Tammy. She had called the state police again, and this time they paid a visit to the TEMAC office to investigate. Tammy told them about the Evelyn Gettman warrant and they checked it out. It was true that the Lewisburg police had done nothing about it. The state police were on their way to Meadow Bridge to search for Tod and track down Evelyn. Tammy had told them she thought Evelyn could have shot Tod. My eyes welled up with tears. "I want my son found," I cried.

"Oh, so do I." Tammy said, but her voice rang hollow.

Rog picked up the extension phone and sat on the edge of the bed with a notebook and pen, taking notes on Tammy's conversation.

"I'll call you the minute I have any other news," Tammy promised. "I'm planning to stay at the TEMAC office around the clock and handle things until Tod is found. Feel free to call me anytime. Don't worry about the business. I'm taking care of everything. I know this must be an awful shock for you, but believe me, Mrs. McQuaid, I'm worried about Tod, too."

She hung up, leaving me staring into the receiver like a simpleton. I couldn't believe this was happening. I began pacing frantically across the floor.

"Jan, stop, please look at me." Rog put his hands on my shoulders and eased me back to the edge of the bed until I sat down. I looked up at him, tears streaming down my cheeks. He walked over to his nightstand, picked up his notepad, walked back to the bed and sat down beside me. "Listening to your conversation with Tammy, I thought that she was very calm during the whole thing. Did you notice that?"

"No," I replied, but after thinking about it, I realized that he was right. "Well, I guess that's true."

"Now think about this," he said. "Have you heard a worried or concerned sound in her voice during any of her conversations?"

I thought that over carefully. "I can't say that I have, other then her first call when I felt she was a little dramatic."

"Why do you think that is?" Rog asked. "It sure makes me wonder. Look, at this point, I'm not sure what's really going on or what to believe. We'll call the police and find out what they might know."

At 11:00 P.M., before we could call the police, Tammy called again. Once more Rog listened with paper and pen in hand, taking notes so that we would have documentation to refer to. Her news wasn't encouraging. She said the police had just left the TEMAC office and according to her they hadn't found anything because it was too dark to search. They had said that they would continue their search in the morning. She was relieved that they had found Evelyn, arrested her, and incarcerated her. Tammy once again assured us we didn't have to worry about the business. She took me by surprise when she mentioned that she had put extra guards on duty, claiming

Evelyn had called and threatened her life. Oddly enough, Tammy said that she had not notified the police about the threatening call.

Rog sat shaking his head and began giving me a signal to hang up. I tried to end the conversation quickly, explaining that we were going to call the police.

"No, you can't," she insisted.

With my tension level on the rise, it didn't take much for me to snap. "Why can't I? Who do you think will stop me?"

"Well, they've gone home for the night," she replied, softening her tone a bit.

"Guess I'll just have to find that out for myself, won't I?"

Rog glanced at me and smiled. I knew what he was thinking. Tammy didn't know me very well. She certainly wasn't going to tell me what I could or couldn't do.

I hung up and called the Lewisburg State Police. The phone kept ringing but I wasn't about to hang up. "Why won't they answer? Where are they? Please, someone answer the phone." Finally a dispatch officer answered. I explained to him who I was and asked to speak with one of the officers in charge of the search for Tod.

"Ma'am, the office is closed for the night," the officer said. By the weary sound of his voice, I could tell that I must have awakened him out of a sound sleep. Still, I wasn't about to give up. I asked to speak with the officers who were searching for Tod, but he told me that they had gone home for the night. I begged him to call one of them.

"Ma'am, I understand, and I'm sorry about your son," he said, his voice filled with genuine sympathy. "I'll see if I can reach Sergeant Johnson or Sergeant Sloan and have him call you. How's that?" I thanked him from the bottom of my heart, and I meant it. "That's all right. I hope they find your son and that he's all right. God bless you, ma'am."

Rog and I lay in bed waiting for the police to call. Rog drifted off to asleep as I sat in bed, wide awake, reading, anticipating, and looking at the clock every two minutes. At 3:30 A.M. when the phone finally rang, it was Sergeant Sloan. Rog awoke and grabbed his notepad and pen. I apologized to Sergeant Sloan for the late hour.

"Not a problem, ma'am," he said with a soft Appalachian accent. "Ma'am, I know how worried you must be about your boy, but I can only tell you that we went to Meadow Bridge and searched around but didn't find a thing. We'll try again as soon as there's daylight."

"Did you find Tod's Bronco? His footprints? Some blood?"

"I'm sorry, ma'am. We found nothing. Not even tire tracks."

"Couldn't you use dogs to search for him?" I asked, desperately.

"Ma'am, we don't have any dogs. Even if we did, we'd need horses to get into the area, but we don't have any horses, either."

If they didn't have dogs or horses to search the area, how would they ever find Tod? For that matter, why mention horses if they didn't have any? My nerves were beginning to unravel. I asked him if Tod might have gone to a farmhouse for help, but Sergeant Sloan sighed and told me that there were no houses in that area, and that no one had seen Tod or heard gunshots. All they had to go on was what Tammy had told them.

That was not much to go on, I thought glumly. I grew quiet for a moment, envisioning my son lying on the cold ground, his blood oozing from his body. Then I panicked. No one was helping me. I was alone. "Why is it that when other people are missing, they have large search parties with flashlights and helicopters and dogs and horses searching late into the night?" I said, practically screaming.

"Ma'am, I understand," the sergeant murmured, "but like I said, we didn't find anything and can't do any more until we have daylight. Ma'am, I really am sorry," he kept repeating.

"Sorry isn't good enough! My son could be bleeding to death unless he is found quickly." I wanted to punch Sergeant Sloan or Tammy Wilson, or a wall. I had never felt so helpless in my entire life. I didn't know what else I could say to the sergeant to make him understand my pain.

Rog took over on the extension and in a very calm voice spoke with the officer. "Tammy Wilson mentioned that you had arrested some girl. What did she have to say?"

"Yes, sir, we did arrest a Ms. Evelyn Gettman on the warrant your son had sworn out against her," Sloan said. "She claims she and her brothers didn't break into the TEMAC office. She also claims she didn't shoot Tod. She said the last time she saw him was in August at the county fair. Miss Gettman is presently incarcerated until we check out a few things."

I interrupted and told Officer Sloan that we were coming down to West Virginia to help search for our son. The officer felt it was best we stay put, and I could only repeat that I was not staying home when my son was in danger and that we would be coming down. I hung up the phone, pulled the suitcases out of the closet and began packing.

"We're staying here," Rog said very calmly. "We'll give the state police a little time and if they don't make any progress, then it's our turn."

"You can bet your bottom dollar I'd get some action started," I growled, slamming a perfectly harmless pink sweater into the suitcase.

"I know you will, Hon," Rog said, pulling me toward him and holding me close to his chest. "I know you will."

I couldn't believe this was happening to us. This only happened to other families that you heard about on TV or read about in the papers. "Rog, I'm scared." I began to cry. Rog wiped away my tears, kissed my forehead and went back to making notes.

"Maybe I'm reading between the lines," he said, "but I don't think the police believe that Tod's in Meadow Bridge."

"What makes you think that?"

"It was something in Sergeant Sloan's voice," he said, "sort of a hesitation or indecision."

I shook my head, trying to clear it. I didn't know what was true and what was a lie. I only knew that my first born was missing, my heart was breaking and Tammy Wilson knew more than she was telling.

# CHAPTER THREE

I was mentally and physically exhausted from too much waiting and not enough knowing. It had been four days and the police hadn't found a trace of Tod or even the slightest single clue as to his whereabouts. It was seven o'clock in the morning and I had already done two loads of laundry, cleaned the refrigerator and was having my fourth cup of coffee when I saw a wren fly past the kitchen window. I couldn't help but smile as I remembered Tod as a five-year-old, kneeling on the ground next to a tiny nestling.

"Mom, I'm glad your here," he said glancing up at me as I came up to him. "How can I get this baby bird to jump on a stick? I want to put it back in the nest." Just then a frantic mother bird, a Jenny Wren, swooped down at Tod. "Hey, I'm trying to save your kid!" Tod shouted at her.

"Tod, she thinks you're trying to harm her baby," I said. "She's protecting it just like I would protect you from harm," I explained, lifting him into my arms. "Let's go inside. The mother will figure out how to save him." We watched from the kitchen window and sure enough, the Jenny Wren swooped down, grabbed the tiny nestling's wing in her beak and flew away with her baby.

I began to think that maybe I remembered Tod and the Jenny Wren because it was a sign from God that I too could save my boy. Suddenly Tammy's call shattered my hopeful moment. She told me that the police had just left TEMAC and were on their way to Meadow Bridge to continue the search. She complained that the police were questioning her. She said she gave the police a list of names of Tod's friends, as they had requested. I let it slip that I spoke with

Sergeant Sloan, and Tammy found this very disturbing. She tried to pump me for information but I told her I was on my out and that I would call her later.

"Was that Tammy?" Rog asked as he sat down at the kitchen table.

"How did you guess?" I answered with a smirk "It seems our days begin and end with that woman." Rose joined us, and as we sat talking about Tod and Tammy, I realized that we had been so wrapped up in recent events that we hadn't called our son Jeff and the rest of the family to let them know what was going on. I wanted to call them, but Rog wanted to wait until we had something substantial to tell them. He felt that when the time came, we should drive to Pittsburgh instead of giving bad news over the phone. Jeff and our daughter-in-law Trish were expecting their second child at any moment, and we didn't want to upset them. Rog was right. Besides, I wasn't sure I had the strength to deal with the family's reactions.

Rose hurried off to work and Rog gathered the girls to take them to school and do some errands. I was alone with my thoughts. Try as I might, I couldn't get the image of my son, hurt and bleeding in the wilderness, out of my mind. When Rog arrived home it was around noon and he decided we should call Tammy for an update. I phoned TEMAC and my heart nearly stopped when I heard a man's voice answer the phone. "Tod, is that you?"

"Excuse me, may I help you?" he asked.

Instantly, I realized it wasn't Tod, but before I had a chance to answer him, I heard Tammy's voice chastise the man. "How dare you answer this phone! I'm the only one that answers this phone. Do you understand?"

"Yes, ma'am, I do," the young man answered in a muffled voice.

"Stupid guard," I heard her say. When she learned it was me, her angry tone did not change much. "I keep telling everyone not to answer the phone, but they just don't listen. They don't seem to understand, I'm running the show now." Suddenly she corrected herself and added, "That is, until Tod returns."

"I hope that's going to be soon," I whispered, rubbing my forehead with my fingers.

"Hey, did I mention that Luke is gone too?"

Luke was a big, black, stray dog Tod had found along a mountain roadside. He was in bad shape but Tod nursed him back to health and they became the best of friends. For reasons of her own, Tammy had allowed Evelyn to take the dog. When I asked her why she would allow such a thing, Tammy explained that Evelyn had said the dog was hers and took it when Tod wasn't home. "Here's what I think happened," Tammy said firmly. "Tod went to get the dog back and Evelyn shot him."

When I asked if she had told this to the police, she said no because they didn't seem to believe anything she told them. I mentioned my concern over the police department's inability to find Tod's Bronco, or even any tire tracks. Tammy couldn't understand that either. She once again reminded me that I shouldn't worry about the business, that she was running it just like Tod would have wanted her to.

When our conversation ended, I looked at Rog as he sat holding the extension phone, shaking his head. "It's hard to understand where that girl's coming from or how she thinks," he said, sighing. "It's as if she's pushing a bunch of puzzle pieces together, hoping they'll fit."

Every time the phone rang that day I jumped. Rose found it hard to concentrate at work. She called often, and with each call I could only give her the same answer, "Nothing yet." Rog put in his daily call to the state police headquarters for updated news, only to be told by Corporal Greene, the officer in charge, that the two officers on the case were still in Meadow Bridge, continuing their search.

"Mr. McQuaid, we're doing everything possible to try and locate your son," Corporal Greene assured him, "but we keep going up one blind alley and down another and still have no leads. I promise you, we will be in touch as soon as we have something."

The same questions kept rolling around in my head about not finding the Bronco, and no one seeing Tod, and the police relying only on what Tammy Wilson was telling them. Had they even bothered to question any of the guards other than Carl? If Tammy actually had given the police a list of Tod's friends, as she claimed, did the police question any of them? If so, what did they have to say?

Corporal Greene never mentioned the list.

Tammy made her usual 11:00 P.M. phone call to say the police had just left the TEMAC office. "They told me they may be onto something," she said."

"What might that be?" I asked.

"They informed me there are three people missing from Lewisburg, and they thought there was a possibility that Tod was with them."

"That's interesting," I said. "There's one little problem with that theory, however. With Rog talking on a regular basis with Corporal Greene, I find it strange he hasn't mentioned it to him."

"Maybe he doesn't know," she replied. "I'm only telling you what Johnson and Sloan told me."

Rog sat, writing his notes, shaking his head in disgust. He began giving me the signal to hang up. He was right. "Tammy," I said bluntly, "I've really heard enough for one night," and ended the conversation.

"I'm losing my patience listening to this garbage," Rog said. "I wish we had another source besides the police because that girl gets on my nerves."

It only took Rog seconds to fall asleep once his head hit the pillow, but I lay in bed with Tammy's story about the missing people swimming around in my head. How I wanted to get Corporal Greene on the phone and check out her story, but I knew I would have to wait until morning. I was so exhausted that I couldn't keep my eyes open long enough to do my nightly reading.

Morning seemed to arrive early, and I made my way to the kitchen where I knew coffee would be waiting. After pouring myself a cup, I went into the family room to sit and enjoy the birds at the bird feeder in the backyard while waiting for Rog's return from taking the girls to school. When he came in, I beckoned him to come into the family room. Looking at me, he began grinning. "I can see you're sitting there champing at the bit to pick up that phone and call the police, aren't you?"

"Yes, I'm going to call Corporal Greene and find out if there really are three other people missing from Lewisburg."

"Well, let's do it." We headed for our bedroom where he grabbed his notebook and pen from his nightstand as I began to dial.

"I'm sorry, no news yet," Corporal Greene said. "I know this waiting is awfully hard on you folks, and I sure wish I had something positive to tell you." I told him about my conversation with Tammy about the missing people, and he was completely taken aback. "Folks, I know nothing about three people missing and neither do the officers in charge of the investigation." Corporal Greene couldn't imagine where Tammy got her information, but he knew it wasn't from the police department. I didn't tell him, but I knew where it came from: her imagination!

After the conversation with Corporal Greene, I was so enraged I paced the hallway trying to release my anger. After a while I went into the kitchen where I immediately called Tammy.

"You and Mr. McQuaid talked with Corporal Greene about the other missing persons?" she asked, in a stunned voice.

"We certainly did," I growled. "Why are you telling us these lies and stories? Corporal Greene said that there are no other people in Lewisburg that are missing. Where Tod's disappearance is concerned, the only thing they have to go on is your information. Or misinformation."

I wasn't surprised when she became irate and practically screamed into the phone. "The police did tell me that. What more do they want from me? I'm telling them everything I know, and you too. Corporal Greene is lying to you."

Her outburst frightened me. Tammy, as unreliable as she was, was the only link between Tod and me. She resented the fact that the police might be doubting her, and now I had made it clear that I doubted her too.

While I wondered how to answer her, Tammy changed the subject. It amazed me how she could be raging like a lion one minute and calm as a lamb the next. She said she had talked to Carl to find out what he might know, thinking Tod might have told him where he was going, but Carl knew nothing. I remembered her saying that Carl was the head guard, and felt it was time I talk with Carl. I asked her for his phone number.

"Well, sometimes he's hard to reach. Why don't I have him call you?" she replied. I demanded his number, and this time she gave it to me. Once again, she changed the subject. "Mrs. McQuaid, Tod's grandmother keeps calling and asking for him."

"Which grandmother?" I asked.

"I think it's his grandmother McQuaid. She's called several times because she wants to visit and spend the weekend of Tod's birthday with him. I told her I'd give him the message, but I think I should tell her the truth."

I made it perfectly clear to her that the grandparents knew nothing about the situation, and until we had more information, we didn't want them to know. If we didn't hear from Tod in the next day or so, we were planning to make the trip to Pittsburgh. "All information is to come only from us," I said, stressing nearly every word.

"Yes, ma'am," she said humbly. "I won't tell her anything, should she call again."

Rog being on the bedroom phone, came into the kitchen. He looked at me with his terrier grin. "Oh, boy, I was wondering how long you were going to put up with her excuses. It's obvious she doesn't know who she's up against."

Smiling as I walked away from Rog, I shrugged my shoulders and said, "I can stand on my own two feet you know."

"You're not telling me something I don't already know." Laughing, he went into the family room to read his latest computer magazine. I turned around and followed, sitting down beside him. I wanted to know how much longer we were going to wait before letting Jeff and our folks know what was going on. I was afraid Mom and Dad McQuaid would decide to pay Tod a surprise visit. Tod called his grandparents often, and it was not like him to fail to return their call. Rog laid the magazine down, cupping his head in his hands, "I just don't know. I keep thinking each day he'll return, but that's not happening. I just know he has to be out there somewhere. How I wish he'd call, telling us what his problems are, or whatever it is that has him detained ... if nothing else, just to let us know he's okay."

There was sadness in his eyes, and I could see how the stress was affecting him. He was keeping his feelings bottled inside.

As I got up and walked into the kitchen, it was then I decided it was time to call Carl. Looking through the window into the family room I said, "Rog, how about grabbing your notebook, I'm going to try and reach Carl."

The phone rang several times before an older man's voice answered with a thick, West Virginia twang. It was Carl. I introduced myself and explained Rog was on the extension. "Mr. and Mrs. McQuaid, how I was hoping you'd call me."

I got right to the point and asked Carl if he had any information he could give us about Tod.

Carl sighed. "Folks, I was with Tod the night before, and he never mentioned he was going anywhere to serve a warrant. The only place Tod goes for any length of time is when he visits the girls and you folks, and he always tells me when he's leaving and when he expects to be back." Carl explained that Tod always gave him a phone number where he could be reached for emergency purposes. He thought of Tod like a son and was very worried about him because this wasn't Tod's normal routine. "Something strange is going on in that office, but I don't know what it is," he said. He was upset that Tammy was running everything, including giving him orders. "To be perfectly honest with you," he said, "I'd go as far as to say that Tammy Wilson is one cold-blooded, evil person, and Tod made a big mistake hiring her."

His strong words shocked me. However, I agreed with him.

"Don't you folks worry. I'll manage until Tod gets back," he said. "I'll call you if I hear anything. It's been a pleasure talking to y'all."

Looking over at Rog, I asked, "What do you think? Perhaps now you'll agree, that it's time we go down there and see what's really going on with Tod's business."

"If we went down there, we would sit and wait, just like we're doing here," Rog said.

Why couldn't he understand how frustrated and helpless I was feeling? All these phone calls weren't helping me. I was frightened to think Tammy was running the office; who knew what she was really doing? I kept thinking about Carl's remarks about her. Was she really cold-blooded and evil?

It wasn't until Rose and the girls came in that we realized how late it was. The day had gone by quickly. Dinner was behind schedule, and everyone pitched in, even the girls, who set the table. Having the girls around helped to lift our dampened spirits. We no sooner sat down to eat when the phone rang. I went into the bedroom to answer it, not wanting Elizabeth and Heather to hear me. It was Tammy. I wanted to hear some good news, but as far as the police were concerned, there were still no leads or clues. It was when she said the police told her they thought Tod was staging his disappearance as a publicity stunt that I became furious.

"Tammy, that's ridiculous," I said. "Are you sure you're not just imagining these things? They know Tod has an established business in Lewisburg, not to mention his activities in many of the community organizations. Let's be realistic, shall we? Why would they make such a statement?"

"That's the way they are," she said, raising her voice. "They should have found Tod or, at least his Bronco by now. I'm getting sick and tired of the way they keep giving me the third degree. I'm thinking of hiring a private investigator to search for Tod."

"Absolutely not," I said resolutely. "We don't need anyone else involved." I cut the conversation short, explaining we were in the midst of dinner and I would get back to her.

After dinner Rose began getting the girls ready for bed. They came running into our bedroom, bouncing on our bed to say goodnight. As I hugged and kissed each one, I thought if they only knew how much their daddy loved them. Smiling and trying to perk up my voice, I looked at Heather and asked, "What are you?"

"I'm your brown-eyed beauty," she yelled, jumping off my lap as she proceeded to twirl around the room. She twirled her way back to me as we laughed at her. Heather was tiny and petite with big, brown eyes and a fair complexion. Her short, straight, dark-brown hair with bangs gave her a cute pixie look. She was a little ham who loved to roll her eyes and entertain with nonstop energy.

As I hugged Elizabeth, I asked, "And what are you?"

"I'm your angel star. Why do you call me that, Nanny?"

"That's what I called you the day you were born. Being our first grandchild, you were my little, shining angel star sent from heaven."

Elizabeth was also petite, and she too had a fair complexion. She had beautiful, long blonde hair and pretty blue eyes and, like her daddy, a broad smile and hearty laugh. The girls stood looking at each other and giggled. Just then Rose called, saying it was bed time. They blew me kisses and were gone.

Once the bedtime stories were over and Rose tucked them in, she came into our bedroom, and sat down Indian-style at the bottom of our bed. "What are we going to do? Where do you think Tod could be?"

"Rose, there isn't anything we can do but sit and wait and pray. I don't know where he could be." I only knew another day and night had passed, and still nothing. My desire to go down to Lewisburg grew stronger. I wanted to go to Meadow Bridge and look around for myself. If only I could persuade Rog to go with me.

As Rose walked toward the door, she turned and looked at me with tears in her eyes. "I just wish that Tod would call the girls." Her voice broke on a sob and she hurried off to her own room.

# CHAPTER FOUR

Having a restless night may have had something to do with the way I felt. I slowly climbed out of bed and walked over to the window, enjoying the sunshine and the beautiful gold, orange, and crimson leaves. Hunting season was approaching. This was the time when my dad would have started preparing his hunting gear. Tod would be doing the same. It was a sport they loved and enjoyed together for many years. I stood at the window thinking, "Tod, please come back, wherever you are."

Rog quietly came up behind me, wrapped his arms around me, and asked, "A penny for your thoughts."

I choked up, trying to hold back my tears as he held me close. I felt his love and tenderness. "I'm wondering how I'm going to get through another day," I whispered. "I now know the meaning of 'hell on earth,' because I'm in it."

Leaning over, he gave me a good-morning kiss on my cheek. "I'll go make us coffee. Maybe that will make you feel better."

What I really needed was to go to West Virginia. Why couldn't Rog and the police understand that? The wait was becoming more and more stressful. As I approached the kitchen, I heard giggling and laughing. Rog had fixed the girls breakfast, and they were pouring syrup on their pancakes. My coffee was waiting in my favorite butterfly mug. I joined them, trying to be as cheerful as possible. I decided that today I would ride along with them to school, thinking we had enough time to stop in the park and collect some colorful leaves for them to take and share with their classmates. Elizabeth and Heather squealed and chattered with delight when I told them my idea.

"Great idea! Everyone grab a sweater or jacket, and let's get on our way," Rog said. The girls gobbled down the last bite of their breakfast, and we were off. When we got to the park, the girls busied themselves, trying to pick the brightest colored leaves. As I crackled through the crisp red and yellow leaves, I kept thinking of Tod and how much he loved this time of year.

We dropped the kids off at school, and on the way home Rog turned to look at me thoughtfully. "Would you like to take a ride and really enjoy the leaves?" he asked. "It might help you relax a little."

His heart was in the right place, but I was eager to get home in case we had a call. As I entered the house the phone was ringing, and I quickly ran to answer it. It was my mother. She seemed upset and concerned. Usually I called her every week, but with all that was going on, I hadn't talked with her since her birthday several weeks ago. I apologized and explained I had been busy. Never one to listen to excuses, she reminded me it only took less than a second to push the buttons on the phone. She told me about the beautiful birthday cards she had received from Tod and Jeff and their phone calls to wish her a happy birthday. I was curious to know when Tod had called her, so I asked her.

"It was on the 5th. He is such a doll, he apologized for being a day late," she said. As far as my mother was concerned, the sun rose and set on her two grandsons.

She wanted to continue talking, and I hated cutting her short; but I wanted the phone lines to be open. I made up an excuse that Rog was waiting for a phone call and that I would call her back later in the day.

"Are you all right?" she asked.

"I'm fine," I said, trying to hide my worried feelings and knowing that I wasn't doing a very good job of it.

"Well, you sound different. Is something wrong?"

I should have known: You can't hide anything from your mother. "I didn't sleep well last night, and I'm a little tired this morning," I said, which was the truth. I couldn't tell her about Tod, not yet. It was going to be hard enough having to tell her face to face, should it come to that.

Rog had coffee poured and waiting for me in the family room.

As I sat down to join him, the phone rang again. It was Mom and Dad McQuaid. They were on their speaker phone so both of them could talk and listen. They were calling to find out what was going on in West Virginia. Rog and I looked at each other as my heart sank. They had called Tod several times, leaving a message with Tammy, who told them Tod was out. They couldn't understand why he hadn't returned their calls. Mom was positivc 'that girl' was not giving Tod their messages.

"When we leave a message on his machine, he returns our calls right away, or at least he used to," Mom said. "This isn't like Tod at all."

Frantically I tried to think of something I could say to smooth things over. I explained that Tod was busy installing three new alarm systems and working long hours. Mom wasn't buying into that excuse since Tod used to return their calls right away, no matter how many alarms he was installing. They wanted to spend Tod's birthday with him, on the 21st of October. Rog glanced at me, a concerned look on his face. All I could do was shrug and give him a look of helpless frustration.

"I wouldn't pull any surprise visits," Rog advised his parents. "If we talk with Tod, we'll have him call you."

"It's that girl, isn't it?" Mom McQuaid said. "She's not giving him my messages. I thought she was an uppity little thing when I first talked to her."

I couldn't help smiling as we hung up minutes later. "Rog, I have never, ever heard your mom speak in anger, but oh, boy, Tammy is on her list today, isn't she?"

Rog laughed as we headed back to the family room to finish our now cooled-down coffee. Rog picked up his computer magazine and began reading. Sipping my coffee, I curled up on the sofa, trying to get into my novel. I found myself reading the same line over and over. I couldn't concentrate. It was hard being far away and relying on phone calls with a peculiar woman to keep on top of what was happening to our beloved son. Still, there was no one else to go to. I felt as if I were caught between a hard rock and another, harder rock.

The wall clock chimed noon. Rog offered to make lunch and had no sooner walked into the kitchen when the phone rang. It was

Tammy. Rog picked up the kitchen phone while I went to listen on the bedroom extension.

"I hope you're calling with some good news," I heard him say.

"I wish I could give you good news, but the police just left here, and I'm afraid I have to tell you they have officially declared Tod missing," Tammy said slowly. "There will be articles in the papers and his picture on TV, and the police will continue searching. Other than that, I don't know what else to say. I'll call you later." She hung up abruptly.

"No!" I screamed, as Rog entered the bedroom. "He can't be declared missing." Tears began rolling down my cheeks.

Rog cried out as if he'd been struck in the face. He sat down on the edge of the bed, lowered his head, and wept into his hands. "I refuse to believe he's dead!" he kept repeating.

In a few days Tod was going to be thirty-six years old. He was full of life, filled with laughter and love, and had many wonderful, happy years ahead of him. He had to see his daughters grow up, attend their school plays and recitals, see them in their first prom gowns, and later, their wedding gowns. He had to be a part of their lives. He couldn't be declared missing! I walked around the bed and sat down beside Rog. We wrapped our arms around each other, trying to comfort one another through our tears. "We must keep praying, asking God to give us the strength to get through this and to bring Tod back safely to us," Rog whispered.

I could only nod.

I called Rose at work, trying to explain Tammy's call, but my emotions took over and I began crying again, so hard that I couldn't speak clearly. Rog made an attempt to take over for me but he wasn't much better. "I'll be right home," Rose said.

The minute she walked in the house the crying began again. We sat and talked about the news release and TV coverage. Immediately, Rose thought of something that hadn't occurred to Rog or me. Our niece Jody lived in Charleston and might see the TV coverage or possibly read of Tod's disappearance in the newspaper. She would surely call her parents to find out what was going on and question why she hadn't been called. We now had to call Rog's brother Bob and sister Carolyn, but before making those calls, Rog dialed the Lewisburg state police, just to confirm Tammy's statement.

"Yes, Mr. McQuaid, he's been declared missing," Corporal Greene said. They had a few suspects, but he was unable to go into any details since Sergeant Johnson and Sergeant Sloan were still investigating the case. "I know you folks are under tremendous stress. We hope to have some news for you soon."

Rog informed Corporal Greene we would be making a trip to Pittsburgh to inform our families and gave him the necessary phone numbers where we could be reached. After hearing what Corporal Greene said, all of Rog's hopes seemed to vanish. He closed himself in the computer room, and I could hear him weeping.

I went into the family room and sat looking out into the backyard, watching two cardinals at the bird feeder as tears continued streaming down my face. *It has to be some terrible mistake,* I thought, over and over. Tod couldn't be dead. He just couldn't. Rose came in and joined me, wiping her eyes and sniffing.

"Tell me it isn't true, that Tammy Wilson made this whole thing up," Rose said.

"I'm afraid it's true," I whispered, continuing to watch the bright red male cardinals take turns chasing one another from the feeder. "What I find so amazing is how calm Tammy was when she called with the news. How could she be so unruffled at a time like this? Everything with her is so cold and matter-of-fact. I just don't understand her."

Rog joined us in the family room. His eyes were red and swollen, and his voice cracked as he spoke. "I guess it's time we make the necessary calls. I can't bring myself to call Jeff just yet, so we'll call my brother and sister first."

Our calls brought on more tears as we broke the news. We asked Bob and Carolyn to notify their families.

"Now, to call Pittsburgh," Rog said. "I never wanted to make these calls, but there is no avoiding them now." His voice continued to crack. He called Jeff, explaining our plans to come visit. My dear husband's voice began to quiver, and finally he could no longer hold back his emotions. He broke the news about Tod's disappearance to Jeff, suggesting that it might not be a good time to tell Trish. Jeff was shocked by the news, but he agreed not to say a word about it to Trish. He mentioned that Trish was a little stressed out waiting for the baby, and I'm sure the news about Tod added to Jeff's stress level tremendously.

"This is incredible!" Jeff gasped. "I can't believe Tod is missing. What can I do? If there is anything at all I can do to help you and Mom, just name it."

"Honey, right now you need to take care of Trish," I told him.

There was sadness in his voice as he quietly said, "Mom I don't know what to say, I'm so sorry. I'll look forward to seeing you, and we'll talk when you get here."

Rog's next call was to his folks. He told them in a halting voice that we had decided to get away for a few days and visit them. If we could reach Tod, we would continue on down to Lewisburg for a few days. They were happy with the news of our coming to visit and mentioned they, too, wanted to visit Tod and were still waiting to hear from him. Not knowing what to say, Rog just ended the conversation by telling them we would see them soon.

Rog sat quietly while I called my mother. Not knowing the circumstances, she was delighted to know that we were coming home and wanted to plan a big lunch for us. How I dreaded having to tell her about Tod. She had lost my dad and all her siblings, and now her grandchild was declared missing. I knew she would be extremely emotional. I also knew that after breaking the news we'd have to pack up and leave for Lewisburg. I told her I would call her as soon as we arrived at the McQuaid's, and our cheery good-bye belied the way I felt.

I was anxious to know about the TV and newspaper coverage and also prepare Tammy for our arrival in Lewisburg in a day or two. I dialed TEMAC's number, and Tammy answered on the first ring. Upon hearing my voice, she told me that Tod's picture had been in the paper and on TV. I assumed they gave a good description of him: 5'11" with dark brown hair, blue eyes and weighing approximately 160 pounds. I asked if they mentioned the silver and gold chains Tod wore around his neck. Tammy wasn't sure, but would see that the police had that information. I mentioned that the newspaper and TV coverage would be the break we've been waiting for, hoping someone would report seeing Tod's Bronco. Then, in her calm, cool, matter-of-fact manner that irritated me so much, she dropped a bomb that made a huge explosion in my mind and rattled my sense of reality.

"Oh, he didn't take his Bronco."

For a moment, I thought I heard her wrong. We had discussed the missing Bronco several times, as well as how we couldn't understand why it hadn't been found. My heart began pounding, and I wanted to scream. Was this just another way of throwing me off balance? Why did she keep doing this? "What are you talking about? He didn't take his Bronco?"

Continuing calmly, Tammy explained that she was concerned because Tod didn't take his wallet or gun either, and he always took his gun for protection when he went to serve a warrant.

"Tammy, you and I were discussing the missing Bronco," I interjected, forcing myself to lower my voice. "And now you're telling me he didn't take it? For once in your life, girl, would you mind getting your stories straight and start telling me the truth?"

"Well, at first he did, but he brought it back."

"Didn't you see him when he brought it back?" I asked.

"He didn't come into the office," she replied.

"You're telling me he brought the Bronco back and didn't come into the office?" I felt reality shifting back and forth rapidly, as if someone were channel surfing on a cosmic television. "Didn't you think he would have had an explanation as to why he was returning it?"

"I had gone home by then, so that's why I didn't see him," she replied. "But the Bronco is in the parking lot here at TEMAC, so he must have brought it back."

My anger began to take over as the tension increased. "How did he get to Meadow Bridge?" I asked. "I'm sure he didn't walk."

"He probably rented a car," she answered smugly.

I couldn't believe what this kid was telling me. "That's absolutely ridiculous. Tod owned three Broncos, and there was no way he would spend money to rent a car." At that point, I realized that Tammy was lying again. I totally lost my cool and began screaming at her. "Damn you! You stupid girl! You said you've told the police everything they wanted to know, but you haven't told them about the Bronco, have you?"

"Not yet, but I plan to," Tammy said. "Oh, by the way, Luke is back."

"I don't give a damn about Luke!" I yelled. "All I care about is my son."

"I found him wandering in the street. The dog, I mean." she said.

I paused to catch my breath, almost too furious to speak. "I suppose he found his way back from Evelyn's place at Meadow Bridge all by himself, or perhaps someone drove him back?" I asked sarcastically.

"All I know is, I found Luke wandering in the street," she said. "Maybe Evelyn dropped him off. Remember, I told you she called and threatened me."

Tammy still sounded so calm and smug that I wanted to reach through the receiver and wrap my hands around her neck. *Give me a minute and I'll start threatening you!* I thought. She then proceeded to go off on yet another story. "The police think Tod is mixed up with a group in Florida, and that's where he could be."

I looked over at Rog and rolled my eyes. He threw his free hand in the air in a gesture of frustration. I couldn't help but wonder if Tammy even realized what she was telling us. "Tammy, where do you think the police are getting their information that you claim they're telling you? If this thing about Florida is true, why didn't Corporal Greene mention any of this to us?"

Tammy paused, as if thinking deeply. "Maybe Sergeant Johnson and Sergeant Sloan are the only ones that know about it," she offered. She apparently believed what she was saying. She must have sensed my skepticism, because she added, "I am telling you the truth. I know it sounds odd, but it's the truth."

"Frankly, Tammy, I don't believe you," I said. "I'll just have to see what Corporal Green has to tell us about all this."

"The police could be making these things up," she said quickly, and I realized at once that Tammy didn't want me to ask Corporal Greene about the Florida matter.

I had had my fill of Tammy and didn't want to keep in contact with her, but I didn't have much choice. I knew that until Tod was found, it was necessary to communicate with her, or at least try to. I motioned to Rog, and he began to explain our arrival in Pittsburgh the next day, telling her that the police would have phone numbers to reach us and she could expect us in Lewisburg the following day. She asked him if we would call her with phone numbers just in case she needed to get in touch with me.

"I'll have to think about that," Rog said, ending their conversation. As he hung up, he looked over at me, shaking his head with a look of disbelief. "That Tammy is some piece of work, and taking notes on her conversations is mind boggling." he said. "It's like transcribing a fantasy novel."

*A bad one at that,* I thought.

# CHAPTER FIVE

I was always excited whenever I packed for our trips to Pittsburgh, but this trip was different. I wasn't looking forward to the journey at all. I thought of Mom McQuaid, busy in the kitchen baking her wonderful coffee cakes and apple pies, and my mom planning a luncheon menu and setting the table a day early. I knew the happiness sparked by our arrival would soon change into a dark cloud of worry.

It had been over a week and still no news of Tod's whereabouts. It was getting harder for me to cope with the situation. I couldn't give up hope that he was still alive. I stopped packing as I reached for his picture on my dresser. I sat on the edge of the bed, looking at it. He was such a handsome guy. I could hear him laugh, and say, "You're the best, Mom." I held his picture close to my breast, longing to put my arms around him and hug him. I couldn't bear the thought of losing him. I was also worried about Jeff, who had to keep the news of Tod's disappearance bottled up inside, unable to share it with Trish.

As I packed a silk blouse my mother had given me for Christmas, I grew afraid at the thought of what I had to tell her. After all, she was alone now. Remembering the trauma and grief she went through when my dad was in the hospital dying, I knew this wasn't going to be any easier for her. Rog's parents had each other, at least; on the other hand, they were older and more fragile.

"Can I help you?" Rog asked as he came in and took his suitcase out of the closet.

"No, I'm fine," I answered. I could see he was wearing down. He seemed to have aged over the past few days; his hair was grayer and the laugh lines around his eyes more pronounced. He was worried about Tod, yet he continued putting up a good front for my sake. He walked around to my side of the bed and stood watching me. "Rog, I feel like I'm on a roller coaster; one minute I'm up and the next minute I'm down. You, you're the strong one who's calm and thinks clearly. Why is that?"

Putting his arm around me and kissing me on the forehead, he said, "Somebody has to take care of you." He reached over and picked up Tod's picture that was lying beside my suitcase. "We have good-looking sons, don't we?" He took Jeff's picture from my dresser and he held the boys' pictures side by side.

I looked up at him and whispered, "Rog, I want our family to be complete."

His eyes filled with tears as he replied, "Jan you'll never know how much I want that too."

Just then there was a soft knock on the door and a little voice called, "May we come in?" Elizabeth and Heather came in with downcast faces. They didn't like the thought of us going away and were hoping they could go with us. I promised them that they could come with us on our next trip to Pittsburgh, which seemed to satisfy them. They gave us a kiss and hug goodnight, and like a flash, were gone. After the girls had started up the stairs, Rose came in. Jokingly I looked at her and said, "Next!"

"I don't need a kiss good-night but a hug will do," she said.

"I thank God for those two little ones. They're helping to keep me sane. I am so grateful you're with us," I said as I hugged her.

As she left, I resumed packing and began thinking about all the families with missing children. You hear about those children and read about them and see their pictures on television shows and milk cartons. But suddenly, when your child is one of them, it's only then that you know the weeping and suffering and awful heartache that their families go through.

The morning dawned gray and dreary, just the way I was feeling. As we got on our way, Rog turned on the car radio to our favorite station, which played wonderful Big Band music from the forties and early fifties. I leaned back on the headrest, listening to Benny Goodman playing "Mood Indigo." It reminded me of wonderful, happy times in my life. What I wouldn't have given to have some of that happiness in my life again.

We reached the Pennsylvania turnpike and lost the radio station. I could sense Rog looking at me. "Are you okay?" he asked.

I didn't want to look at him. Struggling to keep my voice under control, I said, "I want to turn around and go home, or skip Pittsburgh and go straight to Lewisburg."

Rog approached a rest stop, pulled in and stopped. He got out of the car and began walking around the parking lot. He seemed tense and frustrated. After a while he climbed back in the car and faced me. From his expression, I wasn't sure what he was going to say.

"Jan, how many times have we talked about this not being the type of trip we wanted to make?" Rog murmured. "We both know the problem facing us is one that can't be told to our parents over the phone. It's going to be shocking enough telling them to their faces. I'm worried about our parents and how they will react. I'm sure you're experiencing those feelings too, and with the three of them up in years, giving them this kind of news doesn't make it any easier on them. So, for their sake, we have to be the strong."

I mulled over what he had said for a minute. "I'll try, but no guarantees," I said.

"Good enough." He started the car and got back on the road.

The next thing I knew we were arriving in Aspinwall. I was anxious to call Jeff, as well as have Rog call Corporal Greene for an update on the investigation. Passing the front of the McQuaid homestead, I thought that the three-story, white Victorian house still looked the same as when I had last seen it. It was our lives that had changed drastically.

Mom and Dad came out to greet us with beaming smiles: Dad in his favorite straw hat and brown, button-down sweater and Mom in the blue, hooded sweatshirt we had given her several Christmases ago. I smiled as I jokingly asked if she was preparing for snow.

"No, but our weather has been cold and very windy." she said, peeking into the back of the car. "I thought for sure you'd have the girls with you."

"Not this trip, but I brought some updated pictures."

As they helped carry our luggage into the house, we entered the kitchen, where we smelled the wonderful aroma of homemade cinnamon coffee cake and apple pie. Dad and Rog continued down the hallway while I detoured through the dining and living room, checking to see if anything had been changed or added. It was an interesting home that had a warm feeling throughout and was filled with antiques and knickknacks of all kinds. The large living room window was crowded with African violets and white begonias in full bloom. I went up to the second floor and entered the bedroom we usually slept in. Rog and I talked and decided to break the news as soon as possible. Rog put his hands on my shoulders. "Let's go. You'll be fine," he said

As we reached the bottom of the stairs, Rog went into the kitchen while I walked to the phone to call my mother. When my mom heard my voice, she was delighted we had arrived safely. Her first question was, "When will I be seeing you?"

I told her to expect us around 6:00 P.M. Her other concern was making sure we were still planning on lunch the following day. I assured her would be there and our plans were to leave for Lewisburg sometime in the early evening. "Mom, we have to talk. I will explain everything when we see you."

A voice from the kitchen called, "Your coffee's getting cold."

Sitting down, looking across the table at these loving parents, I wondered how Rog was going to be able to tell them the news that would surely devastate them. We brought them up-to-date on the girls by showing them the pictures I brought along. Looking at the pictures, they marveled at how the kids had grown. Mom thought Elizabeth had my little nose and looked like me but could see Tod in her too. She thought Heather looked just like Rose.

When Mom began to refill our coffee cups, Rog made his move. "Jan and I made this special trip because we needed to give you this news in person," he said slowly, carving every word. "It is also our reason for leaving tomorrow to go to West Virginia. This is not going to be easy, because this is not good news, so please bear with me."

My heart began to pound as I reached out and laid my hand on Rog's thigh. He put his hand on top of mine and squeezed it. He hesitated, as though he wasn't sure how to begin to say what had to be said. Complete silence filled the kitchen. "We have been informed that Tod is … missing." His parents both gasped quietly, and the color drained from their faces. Rog went through the whole story.

Mom bowed her head, slowly shaking it back and forth. Dad reached over and held her hand. They sat in silence. Then, in his soft voice, Dad looked at us and asked, "How could this happen?"

None of us had the answer to that.

We sat in silence for a few minutes, then Dad looked at us and said, "I think I can safely speak for Mother and me to tell you the sorrow we are feeling right now for our Tod. We also realize the worry and heartache you must be suffering. What can we possibly do to help the two of you?"

I looked at this man with sadness in his eyes, knowing the despair he was feeling. Yet it was so typical of him to want to help us. Now I knew where Rog got his strength.

"Jan and I are deeply touched by you and Mom wanting to help," Rog said quietly, "but there is nothing any of us can do but sit and wait."

Rog got up to call the police in Lewisberg, and I busied myself clearing the table. Dad got up from the table with his head bent down and slowly walked into the living room. Mom began washing the dishes in the sink. As I dried, I could see she was in deep thought. We stood together in utter silence, like statues, like shadows. She had been a very special person in my life. I loved her dearly and considered her a second mother, more than a mother-in-law. I quietly walked over to the doorway and peeked into the living room to check on Dad. He was sitting in his chair with his head bowed down low. I walked over to him, putting my hand on his shoulder. "Dad, are you all right?"

Never looking up, he replied, "I'm very worried about Tod. There are many evil people in this world today that harm others for no reason at all, and I hope Tod hasn't met up with one of them. I hope our boy is found alive and well."

I knew by the tone of his voice he was feeling helpless, just the way I felt. I began biting my lip to hold back my tears as I turned from him and went back to the kitchen to find Mom washing the same dish she had been washing when I left. "Mom you're going to wash those daisies right off that plate," I said, smiling at her.

"Oh, dear!" We laughed as she handed me the plate. Then she burst into tears. I put my arms around her, trying to be strong.

Rog hung up the phone and we joined him in the living room. Corporal Greene had said they still didn't have anything for sure, but they might be on to something. But, again, because of the continuing investigation, they couldn't give out any information. "I find this whole situation as frustrating as hell," Rog said.

I put in a call to Jeff, hoping he would be in his office. Sure enough a voice answered, "Jeff McQuaid here."

He and Tod sounded so much alike for a minute it startled me. The first thing he asked was, "Any news about Tod?"

I hated having to tell him nothing had changed. I explained our plans for going to West Virginia unless Trish went into the hospital. In that case we would postpone our trip for a day, as long as nothing major developed in Lewisburg. "I understand, Mom," he said, his voice tinged with sadness. It made me want to put my arms around him to let it him know it was all right. I didn't want him to feel torn. I insisted that we were doing okay, and was very careful not to tell him that I certainly didn't feel okay.

Dinner was exceptionally quiet. After dinner, I called my mother to let her know we were on our way. In the car I was on pins and needles thinking of an easy way to explain this crisis. I decided just to explain that Tod was missing and that the police were searching for him.

My mom was standing at the window watching for us. We were no sooner inside than she asked if I had brought any pictures of the girls. We walked through her dining room area, and it was just as I knew it would be. The table was all set for the next day's luncheon. I smiled, complimenting her on the pretty blue tablecloth and matching napkins. "Wow, new dishes too?" I said, teasing.

She grinned sheepishly. "I bought them especially for your visit." If my dad had been there, he would have made some teasing remark. I felt the emptiness without him.

We followed her into the living room. Many pictures of Tod and Jeff and the three great-granddaughters graced the end tables. We sat down, and I took the pictures from my purse and handed them to her. As we sat and talked, the conversation got around to the next day's plans. I explained that we planned to spend the morning with her and head for Jeff's in the afternoon, and from there leave for Lewisburg.

"You never stay long on your visits," she huffed. "I'm sure Tod wouldn't mind if you went down there later in the week." Rog was sitting in the reclining chair across from me. He nodded, as if to say, "Here's your opening."

"Mom, there's something I have to tell you." I began fidgeting with the seam on the sofa. "This is not an easy time for Rog and me, and it's not going to be easy to explain. We are going to West Virginia tomorrow because Tod is missing." I went on to tell her everything I knew.

When I finished, she stared at me, puzzled. "What do you mean Tod is missing?"

"Just that, he's missing." What more could I have said that I had not already said?

My mother's face turned white as I repeated the events in greater detail. "You should have told me sooner," she said at last. Then she made me promise to keep her informed about any developments, big or small. "How about something to drink?"

"A glass of wine would be nice," I replied, and Rog agreed.

Once she was in the kitchen and out of earshot, I asked Rog what he thought was going on with her. He didn't know, but he agreed that it wasn't like her to remain so calm in the face of calamity. I had asked God to give her strength to be able to handle what I had to tell her, but wow! This was like a miracle.

"Here we are. Hope you like this," Mom said, all smiles as she came out of the kitchen carrying a tray. "I put a little snack of cheese and crackers together just in case you're hungry." She paused, and the phony smile slid from her face. "Jan, I can't get Tod out of my mind. I can't believe he's been missing for eight days. I'll be worried sick until they find him."

It had been a long day and I was beginning to feel tired. I had mixed emotions about leaving my mother, but she seemed to be doing as well as any of us. As she walked us to the door, she said, "I hope they find Tod soon."

"I hope so too, Mom."

# CHAPTER SIX

I awoke sometime later in the darkness. A quick check of the digital clock revealed that it was just past five. Not wanting to awaken Rog, I climbed out of bed quietly. When I reached the first floor, I found Mom McQuaid sitting in the living room, reading. She had gotten up at four o'clock and had what she called her "first breakfast." She looked tired and probably could have used another couple hours of sleep. Now that I was up, she would have her "second breakfast" with me. She said she had been awake most of the night thinking about Tod. We no sooner sat down at the kitchen table than Rog joined us. It wasn't long before we heard more footsteps.

"Any phone calls this morning?" Dad asked as he appeared from the hallway.

"I'm afraid not," Rog replied.

I wanted to put off calling Tammy as long as possible, then changed my mind and decided to get it over with before going to my mom's for lunch. I planned to avoid any lengthy conversation with her if at all possible. At 8:00 A.M. on the dot I called Tammy at the TEMAC office and gave her my mom's phone number. Then I reminded her that we would be arriving at the office the following morning. I was about to hang up, but Tammy had other ideas.

"Mrs. McQuaid, have you talked with the police lately?"

"Yes, and as you are well aware, nothing has changed."

"I still can't understand why the police haven't come up with something," she said, her voice full of concern that I didn't think was genuine. "I hope you won't be mad at me, but I hired a PI from Meadow Bridge to help find Tod. I'm sick and tired of the police not doing their job. This fellow knows the area very well."

I was angry she had taken it upon herself to hire a P.I. after I had told her no, if indeed she had done so. She began to speak again, but I cut her off. I didn't want to hear her excuses, and I didn't have the patience to listen to anything else she had to say. As quickly as I could without being overtly rude I ended the conversation with her, hanging up the receiver just a tad too hard.

"She got to you again, huh?" Rog asked.

"She does just as pleases. She says that she hired a P.I. If she did, is he really is a P.I.? It's only her word. And who does she think will pay for his services?"

"Look out, Lewisburg." Rog said, holding up his hands, as if fending off an angry assailant. "I can tell it's going to be one of those days."

Since I hadn't slept well, I went back upstairs for a nap. However, the minute my head touched the pillow my thoughts went into motion. I imagined Tod lying somewhere in the mountains, too weak to move or holler for help. If only we knew where he had been shot, or if he were shot at all. Why couldn't they find him? Had he really tried to get the dog back? Then there was the question of the Bronco. Each day he was missing made the situation seem hopeless. Why was I thinking this way? I had to believe he would be found.

Later, when we arrived at my mom's, everything was ready, as I knew it would be, including fresh cut flowers on the table: yellow roses, my favorite.

As we sat in the living room and talked, Rog was feeling so weary he excused himself and went to the bedroom to lie down. Mom and I continued talking about Tod, and finally she could no longer hold in her feelings and broke down and cried.

"I just couldn't bear it if I lost Tod." She got up and walked over to the picture window, holding back the curtain to look out, as though she were looking for him. Reaching for a tissue from the box sitting on an end table, and wiping her silent tears, she walked away from the window and glanced at the clock.

"It's 11:30. You sit and relax while I get lunch ready." She headed for the kitchen, still wiping her eyes. Within minutes, the phone rang.

"I'll get it," I yelled, loud enough so my mom could hear me. I was hoping the call was from anywhere but West Virginia.

"Hi, Mrs. McQuaid, this is Tammy. I need some information."

"What kind of information?" I asked suspiciously.

"I need the name of Tod's dentist."

"What do you need that for?" I asked, suddenly very nervous. Dental records were often requested to identify a corpse.

"The police may be on to something," she replied.

"What does his dentist have to do with it?" I asked.

"I don't know. They just asked me to call and get that information from you."

"Did they find Tod?" My heart began pounding.

"I really don't know," she said in an annoyed tone of voice. "I'm only doing what the police asked me to do."

I gave her the name of the dentist in Springfield whom Tod had seen years ago. If he had a dentist in Lewisburg, I had no idea who he was. "What's going on down there?" I asked.

"Hey, I don't know, okay?" she said, continuing to sound very short-tempered. "I'll give this information to the police and get back to you shortly."

I had a gut feeling she was lying, but before I had a chance to ask any more questions, she hung up. Why hadn't the police contacted us if they needed that information instead of having Tammy Wilson do it?

Calling from the kitchen, my mom asked, "Who was on the phone?"

"It was for me," I yelled back.

She stuck her head out of kitchen doorway. "Was it news about Tod?"

"No," I answered.

I couldn't bring myself to tell her the truth. I knew she would have to know sooner or later, and I wanted it to be later. It was less than five minutes before the phone rang again. My mom was still in the kitchen. Once again I yelled, "I'll get it."

When I said hello, Tammy said, "Mrs. McQuaid, they found Tod."

"Oh, thank God." I felt relieved. Then suddenly an awful feeling of dread and fear swept over me. I held my breath. "Is he alive?"

Just as cold as a block of ice, Tammy Wilson answered, "No."

My heart began to pound. My knees became weak. I started to shake all over, and I couldn't speak.

In a sharp tone of voice, Tammy asked, "Hey, did you hear what I said? Are you still there?"

All I could manage to get out was, "We're on our way," and hung up. My body went into shock. I was freezing, and my hands shook. I couldn't get my legs to move. I felt numb, as if I had been stuck by a bolt of lighting. I wanted to scream my lungs out and began biting on my lower lip to keep from crying out. I needed to get to Rog and headed for the bedroom. He was in a sound sleep, but when I touched him he jumped like a spooked horse. Putting my arms around him I whispered, "Rog, Tammy called. They found Tod. He's dead. She said he's dead. I don't want him to be dead!"

Rog sat straight up. "What?" he shouted.

"They found Tod, and she said he's dead!" I began quickly explaining Tammy's phone call.

"Jan, please slow down. I can't make heads or tails of what you're saying."

I was all choked up, trying to explain what Tammy had said. How was I going to be able to get through the next hour, facing my mother and keeping myself under control? I wasn't sure I could do it.

"Please, I don't want to tell my mom yet," I murmured. "Let's go to your mother's and call the police, and when we have all the details, we'll come back. Then I'll explain everything to her." I was ready to jump out of my skin and needed to get out of there. My body shook like a tambourine in the hands of a madman, and my hands felt like ice. My heart was beating so fast. At that moment I heard a light tap on the door. Lunch was on the table. Eating was the last thing I wanted to do, but I needed to appear calm so my mom wouldn't suspect something was wrong.

We went into the dining area and sat down at the beautiful table setting, but all I could think about was getting through the next hour. I put very little on my plate. The only thought whirling in my brain was, "My son couldn't be dead." It just wasn't true, and it was another one of Tammy's lies. It had to be.

"Is that all you're going to eat?" Mom asked as she looked at my plate.

"I guess I'm not very hungry." I said, trying to keep my voice in control. I was holding everything inside of me with every ounce of strength I had. I wanted to scream and desperately needed to get out of her apartment. When she went into the kitchen, I leaned over to Rog, urging him to hurry and eat so we could leave. The poor guy! I dropped the biggest bomb ever to hit us, and now I was asking him to gobble down his food. He seemed to be in a daze. I wasn't quite sure if he was fully awake or, like me, in shock. My mom seemed to be watching my every move. I had the feeling she knew something was wrong and didn't want to ask. When Rog was finally done, I jumped up and began clearing the table.

"Mom, I'm sorry we have to eat and run. Thanks for the delicious lunch." I said, giving her a hug.

"How would you know? You hardly ate." she said, frowning. "What's wrong with you? You seem so nervous and edgy and in such a rush. You will call me when you get down to Lewisburg, won't you?"

"Yes, but it won't be tonight."

Rog gave her a hug and thanked her for lunch. Walking us to the car, she continued waving as we pulled out of the driveway, and she yelled, "Have a safe journey."

Once we were on the road, Rog glanced over at me. "I know you're extremely distraught, but do you think you could please explain to me the conversation you and Wilson had?" I began rambling at a mile a minute. "Jan, stop!" Rog shouted. "I'm sorry. I didn't mean to shout, but I can't understand you. Please slow down."

My voice was trembling, and I began again, a little slower, explaining Tammy's first call about the dentist. I was wringing my hands as I related her second call. My tears became uncontrollable. Rog made a right turn to avoid a traffic jam, taking the back streets and making his mother's in record time. As soon as we pulled in the driveway, it was as though Mom and Dad had been waiting for us. They almost ran out of the house to meet us. Mom was annoyed with Tammy for calling several times, asking for me, especially since Mom had given her my mother's phone number each time she called. "What was so urgent that she called here so many times?"

I sat in the car listening. *That bitch*, I thought. She made those calls on purpose. She knew exactly where we were and how to reach me. I got out of the car, and cried out, "He's dead! Tod's been found, and he's dead!" In my dazed state I walked past them into the house, walking straight into the living room, and sat on the sofa, staring into space. My mind was a total blank. Rog, Mom, and Dad followed me, and suddenly I felt Rog next to me, wrapping me in his arms. For a long time the only sound I could hear was my own sobbing.

# CHAPTER SEVEN

Rog called the state police while I sat beside him. Mom and Dad sat quietly at the kitchen table. I motioned for Rog to turn on the speaker phone so I could hear, but he shook his head. He spoke for a while with Corporal Green, and suddenly Rog looked agitated and his eyes became the size of silver dollars. All I remember him saying was, "When did it happen? Who was it? Where did they take our son? Are you sure that's all you can tell me?"

He hung up the phone and began taking deep breaths. That could only mean one thing; he was holding in his emotions. His eyes filled with tears as he reached out and took my hand. Mom and Dad came into the living room, anxiously waiting to hear what Corporal Greene had to say. "It's not good news," he said. I wasn't sure I wanted to hear it. The three of us sat down on the sofa facing Rog.

He took a handkerchief from his pocket to wipe the tears from his eyes. "It's true. Tod was found not alive. A young man entered the police station early this morning and confessed to shooting and killing Tod on October 6th."

We were so sure Tod would return alive and well. How I wanted to believe that. Now, I was being told my son was dead, and I knew eventually that I would have to accept it. But now wasn't that time.

Still breathing deeply, Rog walked to the living room window, keeping his back to us and looking out as he continued wiping his eyes and talking. "They found Tod's body in Ohio, and he was taken to the county morgue in Charleston, West Virginia, where a Dr. Sopher will perform an autopsy." His voice kept cracking as he spoke. "Tod's body will then be transferred to a funeral home in

Charleston. I must call the funeral home to make arrangements for picking up Tod's body, which will be released on Friday, and that's all he could tell me at this time."

I got up and walked over to him. "That's all he could tell you?" I asked, raising my voice. "What about the fellow who confessed? Who was he? Where was he from? Why did he kill Tod?"

Rog sighed. "Corporal Greene wasn't at liberty to release any information. He did make one thing very clear. We're not to give Tammy Wilson any more information. According to him, she's a suspect."

"I knew it," I said, still dazed. My gut had told me all along that she had had a hand in this.

"Well, you were right," Rog said through his tears. "Corporal Greene said that he would give us the details on Thursday."

Mom and Dad sat motionless. I ransacked my mind for ways to avoid the obvious. Maybe the body they had found wasn't Tod's. It could have been a case of mistaken identity. Rog tried to make me understand that dental records had been received from our dentist in Springfield, and they matched the teeth found among the remains.

No! I just couldn't lose Tod. My life would never be the same without him. What was he was doing in Ohio? How did he get there if he didn't take one of his Broncos? My brain felt like one big sieve. Waiting until Thursday to have our questions answered would seem like an eternity.

"Right now, I need to call Jeff," Rog said.

"Why?"

Rog held me tightly. "Jan, I know this is hard, but our son is gone," he said. With that he walked to the phone and called Jeff. I sat there crying. If I believed hard enough, I thought, maybe I could make this all go away.

Rog and Jeff talked for quite a while. Being able to express their feelings and talk about Tod was good for both of them. Rose! I had to call her. How was she ever going to explain to Elizabeth and Heather that their daddy would never come home again?

"Be sure to keep us posted," I heard Rog say. "Give Trish our best and a big hug to Kaitlyn." He hung up, then turned to me and said,

"Good news. Trish is in labor." At that, fresh tears streaked down his face. I turned away before my own tears took hold again.

Then I made the most difficult phone call I ever had to make. I called Rose.

"They found him, didn't they?" she asked, before I even got a chance to say hello.

"Yes." I said, as my voice quivered.

"He's dead, isn't he?"

My silence was all the affirmation she needed. "How are we ever going to tell our girls?"

"I don't know. I wish I did. I don't even know how to tell myself." I told her that the funeral would be in Pittsburgh. Rose said she and the girls would arrive as quickly as she could get them on a plane.

After we hung up, Rog proceeded to make the necessary calls. He called the local funeral director, who agreed to handle all the arrangements for us, including transporting Tod from Charleston. Rog explained that we had some decisions to make before final arrangements could be made and that would get back to him in the morning.

I asked, "What decisions have to be made?"

"We'll talk about it later." he said, "Right now, my question to you is when do you plan to make the trip to your mother's?"

"Oh, my gosh, my mother!" With everything happening so quickly, my mind was blocking out important details. Because it was 6:00 P.M., I wasn't about to call her just then. She thought we were on our way to Lewisburg.

I curled up on the sofa and cried like a child. Rog went outside and kept walking around the yard like a caged leopard. Mom went to their bedroom and closed the door, and I could hear her crying. We all needed our own space for a little while. Dad, being more strong-willed, began making phone calls to all the family members and friends.

We arrived at my mother's at seven. My stomach felt as if it were on fire, and I wanted to throw up. When my mom opened the door and saw us standing there, the color drained from her face. "Why aren't you on your way to West Virginia?" she asked.

"There's been a change in plans, Mom."

The drive back to Aspinwall was quiet, although Rog asked me a dozen times if I were all right. "I don't want you having a heart attack," he said.

Mom and Dad McQuaid were sitting in the kitchen waiting for us. Mom had made a pot of tea, but Rog declined for both of us. I felt like my brain was dead, and I couldn't think straight. That night in bed I tossed and turned and silently cried myself to asleep. Dreaming of Tod woke me. Unable to fall back to sleep, I lay there waiting for dawn. I looked at the clock. It was 5:30 A.M. when I heard Mom going down the stairs. I climbed out of bed, deciding to join her. As I passed the bedroom next to ours, I was surprised to see Rose and the girls sound asleep, all cuddled together in the same bed in the spare bedroom.

Suddenly I heard footsteps on the stairway. It was Rog. "Get dressed. Your new grandchild is on its way."

We sped to the hospital as if we were the prospective parents. The anticipation and excitement we felt as we sat in the hospital waiting room, knowing that we would soon have a new grandchild, helped ease the tremendous stress that still clung to us. For the first time in weeks we had a spark of happiness.

Jeff appeared in the doorway, grinning from ear to ear. "Tierney Sewall McQuaid has arrived," he announced. "Give us a few minutes, and you can come in and see her."

As a nurse passed by, Rog gently touched her arm. "I just had my fourth granddaughter," he shouted with great pride.

"Congratulations," she answered, smiling, as she continued walking down the corridor.

Jeff came in and said, "Tierney is ready for her debut."

We entered the birthing room that looked very much like an ordinary bedroom, and I marveled how much hospital procedures had changed in a big way since Tod and Jeff were born. Trish was smiling, holding our little bundle of joy wrapped in a pink blanket with blue bunnies on it. I peeked under the little cap she was wearing, "Oh, my gosh, we have another redhead," I said.

"I can't imagine who she gets that from," said one of the nurses, looking at me and my auburn colored hair.

I held Tierney, and my heart was filled with love for our new little granddaughter. *The Lord giveth and the Lord taketh away,* I thought. I searched for some trace of Tod in the baby's face and finally decided that her ears were shaped just like his.

We reluctantly said our good-byes and waited for Jeff in the hall, since he had suggested we have breakfast together. Sitting in the hospital cafeteria, Jeff and I listened as Rog explained our plans for West Virginia. He took me by surprise when he said that we would be going to Charleston Friday evening to get Tod.

"I thought all those arrangements were taken care of," I said.

"We have some decision-making to do regarding that," Rog said, again not going into any explanations.

Leaving the cafeteria, Jeff put his arm around me as we walked toward our cars. "Mom, would you mind if I had a few minutes alone with Dad?"

His request took me by surprise. It was so unlike him. "That's fine," I replied.

Gentleman that he was, he held the car door open for me while I climbed in. I looked up at him and gave him a loving smile.

"We won't be too long. I promise," he said. Placing his hand on his dad's shoulder, they walked toward Jeff's car.

I couldn't help but wonder what it was Jeff didn't want to share with me. It was approximately fifteen minutes before Rog returned. He climbed into our car and without saying anything pulled out of the parking space. He didn't seem in any big hurry to share what he and Jeff had talked about.

I broached the subject myself. "What was so secretive that Jeff couldn't share it with me?" I asked.

Rog hesitated. "Jeff is being overprotective of you," he said at last.

"What do you mean, overprotective of me?"

Rog found a parking spot and pulled over to the curb. "During the night, Jeff was able to find a West Virginia TV station where they talked about the shooting," he said.

"What did they say?" I asked with grim anticipation.

"I wish I could break this to you gently, Jan, but I don't know how else to tell you," Rog said with a deep sigh. He took my hand and held it firmly. "Tod was shot in the head."

"No!" I screamed as hysteria set in. "No!" I began to thrash my arms around like an animal struggling for its life. I wanted to get out of the car and just run. Rog grabbed me and wrapped his arms around me and held me tightly against his chest "Who could do such a horrible thing?" I shouted as tears coursed down my face. "I hope whoever he is burns in hell." Rog continued to try to hug me and calm me down. Suddenly, the image of Tammy Wilson flashed in my mind. *She* did it. I didn't know how, but I knew she did it.

We sat in silence for some time. "What do you say?" Rog said at last. "Are you okay now, so I can drive back to Mom's?"

"Yes, I think so." As we drove along, I experienced moments of tranquility, always followed by a fresh burst of tears. Shot in the head! Oh my God! Like an execution!

We arrived back at the house, and Rog remembered he needed to call Tammy to let her know we wouldn't be arriving in Lewisburg until Thursday. He wanted her to inform all the guards to be present at the TEMAC office around three o'clock, not only so that we could meet them, but so we could discuss the future of TEMAC. I was curious to hear what she would have to say, but Rog wouldn't put on the speaker phone. He kept saying, "I told you I don't know. What don't you understand? Didn't you hear what I just said?" He was beginning to get angry. When he hung up as last, he was positively boiling. "That girl has more brass ...," he growled. "She actually asked if we'd take her to Charleston with us so she could see Tod for the last time. That bitch!"

His second call was to the West Virginia county morgue where he spoke with Dr. Sopher. Then he immediately called the funeral director in Charleston. "Yes, we are having him cremated," I heard him say. "What time will we be able to pick up his remains? We'll be there at eight o'clock, Friday evening."

I was stunned. He might as well have hit me with a baseball bat! We hadn't even discussed how to dispose of Tod's remains, so what right did he have to say that we were going to cremate him? Once Rog was off the phone, I began shouting. "I didn't want him cremated," I wailed in anger and despair. "Why didn't you ask me what I wanted?"

In his understanding manner he led me to the sofa. Mom and Dad joined us. "My conversation with Dr. Sopher was not pleasant," Rog said. "Tod's body was very decomposed. Since we couldn't have an open casket, I felt having him cremated was the best thing to do and made that executive decision. We will go to Charleston on Friday and bring his remains back for burial."

I was not happy with his decision and without saying a word, got up and walked up the stairs to the second floor and climbed into bed. I was angry, and bed was my escape. I wasn't aware that Rog was right behind me. He came over to me and sat down on the edge of the mattress.

"Please don't be angry with me," he said softly. "I did what I felt was the right thing to do. Remember, Tod had been lying in the woods for some time, and you wouldn't have wanted to see him as he looked after the autopsy. It would have haunted you for the rest of your life. I love you and want to help ease the pain and heartache you're suffering." Rog bent forward until his head rested in his long, slim hands. "I'm trying my damnedest to cope, and it isn't easy for me. You must accept the fact that Tod is gone, and we will never have him back."

"You don't understand," I said. "A piece of me has died, and something inside keeps eating at me. I know Tod is gone, and you're right. Nothing we do will bring him back. It's hard for me to come to terms with the fact that I will never see him again. I want revenge. I want that son of a bitch to pay for taking Tod's life. I want him to pay for what he has done. Why can't you understand that?" I suddenly felt very frustrated and alone.

"I do understand," Rog replied. "I promise, somehow we'll get through this together." He fell silent and climbed into bed beside me. The familiar spicy smell of his aftershave comforted me. "Try to get some sleep," he said grinning, as he reached up to turn off the light. "I don't want you to get bags under your eyes."

I had to smile. "You're so funny."

He kissed me ever so gently. "I'm glad I can still make you smile," he said. "I love you."

I couldn't argue with that. "Love you, too." I replied as I drifted off to sleep.

The sound of the doorbell woke me. It was nine in the morning. Rog was no longer beside me. He must have slipped quietly out of bed. I lay like a rock, not wanting to get up. I began thinking of Tod's burial, something I really wanted to put out of my mind. Then I noticed the bedroom door opening slowly. It was Rog, checking to see if I was awake.

"There's a whole bunch of people downstairs," he said, "buzzing like bees. Family, friends, everyone. You don't have to come down if you don't want to."

I decided to see who had come to visit, so I threw on some clothes and headed downstairs. Rog was right: The entire house was packed with visitors — relatives, neighbors, and many people I didn't know, all offering me their condolences. I found my mom, who held me and comforted me. She even offered to make all the funeral arrangements and agreed with me that Tod should be buried with my dad, his beloved grandfather. "Thank you," I said. "I hope you don't mind, but I have to get out of here. I can't stand all this racket."

"Yes, it's a bit much," she sighed. "You should go back to your room and get some sleep." I agreed, but when I reached the top of the stairs, for some unknown reason, I walked into Mom and Dad's bedroom and climbed into Mom's twin bed.

I appreciated the peace and quiet of the tidy bedroom with its restful blue walls and white lace curtains. It helped me recall long-gone happy times in this house with Tod and Jeff when they were little. How many times I had to remind them not to slide down the banister! I could still see Tod working in the garden, or swinging his sawed-off golf club that Dad McQuaid made especially for him.

After a few minutes, I heard a soft knock on the door. It was my nephew, Michael. "Aunt Jan, may I come in?" he asked.

"Of course, Mike," I replied.

Michael was a Lutheran pastor, the youngest of Bob and Jan's children. He pulled up a chair to the side of the bed and in his soft, low voice said, "Aunt Jan, there are no words to tell you how sorry I am about Tod. It's been a great shock for all of us. Is there anything at all I can do to help you?"

I looked at this tall, handsome young man, remembering him as a little boy with light blond hair, big, blue eyes and a very expressive laugh. "Mike, as a matter of fact, there is something you can do," I said quietly. I asked him if he would conduct the memorial service and give the eulogy for Tod at the Good Shepherd Lutheran Church. "I know it's not your church, but I have no problem asking Pastor Bob for his permission. I know that's what Tod would have wanted, and that's what I want too. It would mean so much to me, and probably to Tod, too."

We both laughed. "Aunt Jan, if it's okay with Bob, I'll do my best, but it isn't going to be easy for me."

Suddenly, as if on cue, there was a second soft knock on the bedroom door. This time Pastor Bob's face appeared as the door cracked open. "May I join you the two of you?" he said as he came in, pulling up another chair.

*Good timing*, I thought. Being as tactful as I could, I asked him if he would mind if Mike handled the memorial service at Good Shepherd. I explained we would be bringing Tod's remains back from West Virginia late Friday night. I wanted to have a family burial on Monday morning, followed by a memorial service, if the church was available.

Checking in his appointment book, he nodded. "It's fine." I knew my request had taken him by surprise. He hesitated slightly, then began speaking. "I have a big favor to ask of you in return, if it's all right. If Mike doesn't mind, I would like to assist him."

"That's fine with me," Mike answered quickly, sounding somewhat relieved, and soon the two of them were discussing the service plans as though I wasn't in the room. I'm not sure how it all came about, but within half an hour, everyone who had been in the dining room had made their way into the bedroom, continuing to talk up a storm. There was no escape for me now. My sister-in-law Jan came in, announcing that dinner was ready. Then the crowd began clearing out, as my mom came in to say good-bye. "You remember to be careful what you do and say in West Virginia." she said, with a concerned look on her face. "I'll be worried sick until you get back."

"Mom, you're starting to sound like Rog. I'm fine, so stop worrying. Now I'm starting to sound like you." Her eyes filled with tears as she bent over to kiss my cheek, and as she turned and left the room I heard her crying.

# CHAPTER EIGHT

The rest of the day passed by in a blur, and Rog and I went to bed early. At 5:00 A.M. I woke up and went to the kitchen. As I passed the toaster, I glimpsed my reflection in its shiny surface: I looked like a wreck. I hadn't been eating well, and I never got more than a few hours of sleep every night. I walked over to the kitchen window and stood watching the wind scatter the leaves to the ground. "I'm not looking forward to Lewisburg," I said aloud.

As I watched the dying leaves, I thought about the upcoming trip and how much I dreaded going. My sisters-in-law, Carolyn and Jan, had kindly offered to watch Elizabeth and Heather so Rose could travel to West Virginia with Rog, Jeff, and me. Rose appreciated the opportunity, and I was happy she was coming along. Jeff offered to drive so that he and Rose could come back on Friday while Rog and I went on to Charleston. With Rog handling Tod's estate and business, it meant he would be making many trips to Lewisburg, and he made the decision to drive back one of the TEMAC Broncos to use for TEMAC business.

At 6:30 A.M. Jeff arrived, right on time. By then I was dressed and ready to go, as were Rog and Rose. On the trip down, Rog and Jeff got into a discussion about TEMAC. Rose and I were in agreement with Jeff. The business should be sold as soon as possible. Rog made no comment. We crossed into West Virginia, and, as I looked at the vast, rugged mountain peaks, I thought of my suggestion to Sergeant Sloan about wanting to go down and help search for Tod in those mountains. He probably had a good laugh over that. The sad part of it all was that Tod wasn't even where Tammy said he was, so all the searching had been in vain. I kept wondering why Tammy told the police that Tod was in Meadow Bridge. Was it some sort of ruse? What was the motive behind her odd actions? In a matter of hours all our questions would be answered.

We finally saw a sign that said *Lewisburg 12 miles.* The five-hour trip had seemed much longer. Rog remembered that the state police headquarters was located close to the TEMAC office. There was no way to miss it, not with all those police cars parked outside the small, white building. We pulled into the parking lot in the midst of frantic hustling and bustling as policemen came and others went off duty. Rog walked up to the officer behind the desk in the main entrance and asked for Corporal Greene.

"You must be the McQuaid family," the officer replied as he stood up. He was a very tall man with a husky build, light brown hair, blue eyes, and horn rimmed glasses. He extended his hand with a warm smile. "I'm Corporal Greene. Folks, I can't begin to tell you how sorry I am about your son. Please accept my sympathy." He glanced at one of several officers standing close by, watching us, and asked him to fetch a few extra chairs. The chairs arrived, and we gathered around Corporal Greene's desk.

"Let me check and see if Officers Johnson and Sloan are still here," he said in a bullfrog-deep voice. "They're in charge of the case, and I would like you to meet them." He again asked the officer, who continued watching us, to find the other two officers, and within minutes Sloan and Johnson appeared. After introductions and handshakes, they too extended their sympathy. They were ready to go on duty, and Officer Sloan explained that Corporal Greene would fill us in on everything regarding the case.

Looking at Sergeant Sloan, I recalled my outrage with him over the phone and felt I owed him an apology. He was doing his job, and I had taken my frustrations out on him. I walked over to him and touched his arm. "Excuse me for being a very desperate and distraught mother when we talked on the phone," I said in a whisper.

"Oh, ma'am, I understand," Sergeant Sloan replied. "No apology needed. I sure wish we could have found your son alive. I'm truly sorry." Rog thanked him and Sergeant Johnson sincerely, and then the two excused themselves. "Corporal Greene will help you good folks all he can. We'll see you again soon."

Corporal Greene went to his file cabinet and took out a folder. He sat down in his chair, thumbing through the papers, setting certain ones aside. "Like I told you on the phone, Mr. McQuaid, we had a confession from a young man saying he shot Tod on October 6," Greene said. "His name is Roger Cline. Tammy hired him as a handyman for TEMAC. Roger lived in Alderson with his uncle, who happens to be married to Tammy's mother."

He continued to explain the situation. "Roger Cline had been out drinking, came home and told his uncle that he had shot and killed Tod McQuaid. His conscience couldn't bear this burden any longer, and he wanted to turn himself in. His uncle called the police station and told them what Roger had said. The officer on duty wanted to send a few men to pick up the suspect, but his uncle replied that Roger wanted to come in on his own. Roger had told his uncle he took Tod's body to Ohio and explained where the body could be found. Cline's uncle then made a phone call to the suspect's mother, who lives in Ohio, explaining the situation to her. She in turn called her sister, who called the Ohio police. They went to the area in question and found Tod's body. Roger Cline walked in here at 6:00 A.M. and gave us a statement."

Corporal Greene rifled through some more papers and finally seemed to find the one he wanted. "Here's the statement Roger gave us. Would you like me to read it to you?" Rog and I nodded and Greene began reading in a drawling monotone.

"After work, Tod asked me to go for a ride. We drove into the mountains, and Tod began shouting at me, saying how dissatisfied he was with my work. He became very angry with me. I became frightened, jumped out of the Bronco and started running into the woods. Tod ran after me and caught me. We fought. Tod was wearing his gun. I grabbed the gun, and it went off and shot Tod."

*Boy, that sounds convenient,* I thought, through my horror. But Cline's story didn't sound believable to me. I just couldn't imagine Tod getting that angry at someone over a poor job performance. He might feel sad or disappointed, but he was very slow to anger.

"Roger Cline was put under arrest, but his story didn't stand up to the facts," Greene continued, as if he had read my thoughts. "We arrested Tammy Wilson and Harry Joe Johnson, both TEMAC employees. Folks, we believe that your son's murder was premeditated by the three of them."

If there is such a thing as shock on top of shock, that's what I went into. My body began to shake as I sat there, tears streaming down my face. It was bad enough that Tod was murdered, but ... premeditated murder? I felt as if somebody had stabbed me. On top of that was the horrific thought that I had been chatting with Tod's murderer almost every night!

I must have looked like I was about to faint. "Mrs. McQuaid, may I get you a glass of water or something?" Corporal Greene asked, with genuine concern.

I shook my head. Jeff sat quietly looking at the floor, shaking his head back and forth from time to time, his face contorted with sorrow, rage, and disbelief. Rose kept wiping her eyes, whispering, "This can't be really happening, can it?"

Rog sat in silence for a few minutes. Finally, clearing his throat, he asked "What was the motive behind this?"

Greene shook his head sadly. "Mr. McQuaid, here's how it looks to us. Tammy Wilson wanted to take over your son's business, and the only way she could do that was to get Tod out of the picture. The pieces started to fall into place when Roger Cline confessed to shooting Tod on October 6 and never mentioned anyone else being involved. But Harry Joe Johnson phoned us on October 15. He said Tod had called the TEMAC office from Meadow Bridge saying he was shot. Tammy Wilson told the officers that Tod had called the office every day except the last two. None of that agreed with Roger Cline's confession. We knew somebody had to be lying because of the discrepancy in stories and dates. On Wednesday evening, officers Sloan and Johnson made a visit to Harry Joe Johnson while he was on guard duty at the lumber yard. After they questioned him, he confessed, saying he was glad it was over. He implicated Tammy Wilson as the master-mind behind all of it."

I wasn't sure I had heard him right. "Excuse me," I said, "may we go back? Right now my head is swirling, and I need to get the facts straight. You mentioned Harry Joe called the police station to report Tod's call. But when Tammy called me, she was all upset, telling me she had the called the police and no one would believe her."

"Oh, no, ma'am," Corporal Greene said, in a very serious tone of voice. "Any phone call we receive in that manner is taken very seriously and checked out immediately. We never got a call from Miss Wilson. It was Mr. Johnson that made the call. He told the officers Tammy Wilson gave Tod alcohol and put a drug in his drink to knock him out cold, and the shooting took place at Ms. Wilson's residence. Near as we can figure, Roger shot your son, Harry Joe was the 'cleanup man,' and Tammy Wilson did the planning. Based on that, we arrested Tammy and Harry Joe."

The room seemed to spin around me for a minute or two, and when everything stopped moving, I managed to think straight enough to ask a question. "Are you saying that Tammy Wilson and Harry Joe Johnson were arrested last night?" I asked.

"Yes, ma'am," he drawled politely. "We brought Roger in for more questioning. Once he knew the other two had been arrested, he changed his story. He said that he made up his first story about Tod being angry because he didn't want to get anyone in trouble and was planning to take the blame for the whole thing, assuming that Tammy Wilson would leave everyone else alone."

Corporal Greene began to read Roger Cline's second statement slowly and carefully, unlike his quick reading of the first statement. All of us we sat listening, frozen with horror and disbelief.

"I shot Tod, and Harry Joe Johnson and me put the body in the Bronco. I drove to Ohio, where I dumped Tod in a secluded ravine. I poured acid on the body so it could never be identified. Tammy Wilson never wanted it found. Harry Joe cleaned up the room and got rid of the evidence. Tammy told us we would all go to our graves with this secret because it was the perfect crime. My mother lived close to where I dumped the body, and I spent the weekend with her before returning to Lewisburg."

"Corporal Greene, excuse me," Rose said. "I don't understand Roger Cline's remark about Tammy leaving everyone else alone."

"Well, ma'am, it seems Tammy made some remarks to Cline and Johnson, threatening their family members if the two men ever told anyone about this killing."

How could I have been so dumb not to see this girl for what she really was? My instincts had told me that what she was telling me was highly suspicious, if not totally insane. I should have realized that Tammy was weaving a cover-up story for herself. How could I have trusted a word she said? According to the statements we had just heard, Tod's death was an act of premeditated murder, and Tammy Wilson had done the premeditating. If I could have gotten my hands on her at that instant, there's no telling what I would have done.

"That's about all I can tell you folks at this time because Sergeants Sloan and Johnson are still investigating the case," Corporal Greene said. "I suggest you stop in and talk with Rick Lorenson, the prosecuting attorney. He might be able to give you some additional information." The corporal gave us the location of Lorensen's office.

"It's hard to believe there are such evil people in this world that don't think twice about taking another person's life. They mustn't have a conscience," Rog said, his face a mask of pain and disbelief.

"I only wished there had been an easier way to tell you," Corporal Greene said. "I'm so sorry."

We left for the TEMAC office, our heads hanging in sorrow. The office was located on Jefferson Street, the main road into Lewisburg. When we pulled into the driveway, we found just enough room to park behind the three Broncos already parked there. I sat for a few minutes before climbing out of the car, wondering what was going to be in store for us once we got inside.

One of the guards had seen us coming and opened the front door, greeting us with a smile. He introduced himself as Keith as he shook our hands. The rest of the guards were sitting in a circle in the office area, which was filled with cigarette smoke. I noticed a room across the hall opposite the office, where two women stood talking. The twelve guards rose the moment they saw us, introducing themselves and shaking hands with Rog and Jeff while giving Rose and me a hug, extending their condolences.

The last one to hug me was Carl. "Mrs. McQuaid, how I wish I could have met you under different circumstances," he said sadly. "Tod's death has been such a shock for all of us. He was a wonderful young man, and we are all going to miss him."

Seeing the sincere grief in his eyes, I felt my defenses go down, and walked away without a word.

Looking around, I saw that Tod was everywhere in that office. Papers lying on his desk bore his handwriting. A reminder board on the wall was filled with his "to do" list, and the guard's schedule he had made was posted for the month of October. Photos that Tod had taken the day he and a friend went flying over New York City were all framed and hanging neatly on the walls. Overwhelmed with his presence, I walked to the room across the hall, but that only made me feel sadder. It was his living room. I was surprised to find only a sofa and the desk that he and Rose once shared. I was curious to meet the two women there. The older one introduced herself as Beth, and she introduced the younger woman as Rachel Johnson. I smiled and said hello, and with that the pretty young girl named Rachel broke into tears and flung her arms around my neck.

"Oh, Mrs. McQuaid, I'm so sorry. Please don't blame me."

Her actions and comment took me by complete surprise. What would I possibly blame her for? Without saying another word, she turned and dashed out the front door. I stood where I was, completely stunned. "What was that all about?" I asked Beth.

"That was Harry Joe Johnson's wife," Beth replied.

Why was she at the TEMAC office? I wondered. With so much going on, I thought she might have heard we were coming and just wanted to meet us. I couldn't blame the young women for her husband's actions. If anything, I pitied her for what she must be going through.

"Mrs. McQuaid," Beth said, "I was a good friend of Tod's. Actually, I considered myself his mom away from home. I knew you were coming and wanted to be here to meet you, since I feel like I already know you. He was so proud of you and Mr. McQuaid and his little girls. He's going to be sorely missed."

"Thank you," I said, genuinely touched by her remarks.

"I'm sorry that the house is such a mess," she said apologetically. "Tammy let it go completely. It should have been cleaned up before you arrived. Your son didn't live like this."

So far I had only seen the office and the living room. I wasn't aware of what the rest of the house looked like, and I wasn't concerned about it. I was concerned about Tod's pets, though, and asked Beth if she knew where they were.

"The two cats have found a home with a lady across the way," she said with a smile. "Keith is taking care of Luke."

Beth felt that she had stayed long enough and was about to leave, but I wanted her to meet the rest of the family. Since Rog was still talking with the guards, I asked her to show me the rest of the house.

Beth happily complied. "Everything is all on one floor," she said. We walked down the hall past a walk-in closet that Tod had built. I wasn't surprised to see all his suits, shirts, sweaters, and belts neatly hung in order. His bedroom was located on the other side of the closet. I was shocked to see just a mattress on the floor. The box springs and headboard were missing. Where was all the furniture Tod and Rose owned? I knew Tod had taken it out of storage when he moved into this house. There was a full bath off the bedroom, and in the back of the house were a good-sized kitchen, a second full bath and a laundry room. The house needed major repairs, as well as a thorough cleaning. The kitchen stove was covered with grease, which surprised me, knowing Tod never fried anything. The kitchen sink was covered with brown stains and full of dirty dishes. The bathrooms looked as though they hadn't been cleaned in a month.

"Where is all of Tod's furniture?" I asked.

"I really don't know," Beth said, "but I'm sure Carl would be able to answer that question for you. He kept tabs on everything concerning this office."

We walked back to the office, where Rog took time out so I could introduce Beth to him, as well as Jeff and Rose. Just before she left, I thanked Beth for being such a good friend to Tod. "It makes me feel better knowing he had a mom away from home," I said. As she approached the front door, she took a tissue from her purse and began to wipe her teary eyes.

Rog continued explaining to the guards that TEMAC would go on operating, and he would be handling the business until it could be sold. As the guards left, Rog asked Carl to stay a few extra minutes. He wanted him to continue his duties as lieutenant and more or less run the office.

I noticed Keith had gone into the living room and was standing there as though he were waiting for something. I walked into the hallway, and Keith said, "Mrs. McQuaid, could we talk for a few minutes?"

Keith had been taking care of Luke at his home and wanted to keep him. "Mrs. McQuaid, I can't tell you how many times I wanted to talk to you when you called, but Tammy would never allow it. I was here the day I overheard her telling you that Evelyn had taken Luke. That was a lie. Luke was here all the time, and I was tending to him. She treated him very badly."

Keith seemed sincere about wanting to keep Luke, and I saw no reason to deny his request. "Luke is going to miss Tod, but if you can give him a good home, then you should have him."

"I'll take good care of him," he said, smiling from ear to ear. He was whistling as he left the office, and I felt happy to have provided a caring home for Tod's beloved pooch.

Rog and Carl were still busy talking. Jeff and Rose walked from room to room, looking around, exclaiming in disgust about the dirty condition of the house. When the phone rang, I automatically walked into the office and answered it. It was Mr. Morgan, Tammy's father. How did he know we were in Lewisburg? I wondered. His rough, arrogant tone annoyed me as he demanded that we take Tod's "stuff" out of his house.

"What are you talking about?" I asked, raising my voice. "What stuff?"

"The house is filled with your son's furniture," he muttered. "I want it all out of there as soon as possible."

When Rog heard the anger in my voice, he decided to intercede. "I think you better let me handle this call, all right?" he said, striding over to me.

I handed him the phone, saying in a very loud voice, "It's Tammy Wilson's arrogant father."

Rog spoke to him a few minutes, assuring him that we would try to remove Tod's things the next day and promising to call him in the morning. Carl, who was taking in every word, stood in the doorway, shaking his head. Rog got off the phone and looked at us. "Just another thing to add to the to-do list." If anybody had the patience of Job, my husband did. "Why is Tod's furniture in Tammy Wilson's father's house?" Rog asked Carl.

It turned out that Tammy had rented the place from her father. A few days after Tod disappeared, Tammy had the guards move Tod's furniture to her house, telling them she and Tod were moving in together. "I knew then she was up to no good," Carl said.

Jeff came up and rubbed my shoulders like an expert masseur. I was so tense my bones crackled under the gentle pressure of his fingers, but it felt good. "Mom, I know how hard all of this is on you," he said," but please try and stay calm. Come out in the kitchen, and give Rose and me a hand."

Like father, like son, I thought. Always composed and calm.

Rog felt we would need a truck as well as all three Broncos to remove all the items from the Morgan house. He asked Carl to handle that and round up some guards to help. They were to be at the office by 10:00 A.M. Going to the house where our son was murdered would be like pouring alcohol on our open wounds, I thought. How we were going to be able to handle that?

Everyone was beginning to feel hungry. Since we were staying at the Fort Savannah, a well-known historic restaurant and motel in Lewisburg, it was convenient to go there for meals, since it was located right next to the TEMAC office. Upon entering the restaurant we were seated in front of a huge stone fireplace where a warm, glowing fire was burning. It was delightful, but while we were waiting for dinner to be served, the atmosphere became decidedly more business-like. Jeff took out a pen and pad from his pocket and wrote *Priorities* at the top of the page. "Okay, let's put everything in order," he commanded us.

I had to smile; he was so much like his father.

"First thing tomorrow morning," Rog said, "I need to go to the bank and inquire about Tod's checking accounts. I sure hope that Tammy hasn't found a way to get into them." Rog mentioned that Tod might have hidden a will somewhere, so we decided to search the TEMAC office for it. When we returned to the office after dinner, Jeff and Rose and I began our investigation, while Rog began working through the business account records, trying to figure out what damage Tammy could have done in that area. A large file cabinet stood in a corner of the office, cluttered with papers piled on top. I gathered all the papers in a heap and, sitting at Tod's desk, began reading them one by one. I found old guard schedules and everything else that was outdated and unnecessary.

When I had completed sorting through the papers on the top of the file cabinet, I walked down the hall into Tod's clothes closet. Taking a burgundy red sweater off the hanger, I wrapped my arms around it and sat on the floor, holding it close to me. The musky fragrance of his favorite cologne permeated it. He always smelled so good. I would have held onto that sweater forever if I could. When Rog found me, he gently pried the sweater from my grip. "Come on, Jan, I know this is tough on you. We've had enough for one day."

That night at the motel, I slept fitfully, plagued by dreams of chasing a burgundy red sweater that kept dancing just out of my grasp. When morning arrived, we drove to the TEMAC office and found the guards arriving right on time. Carl had rented a fairly large truck. We had no idea where Tammy lived, but the guards directed us to her house, a white clapboard cottage that had seen better days. Mr. Morgan was standing in the yard waiting for us, a tall, slender man in a red flannel shirt, blue jeans, and a battered West Virginia Mountaineers baseball cap. Not speaking a word, he walked to the front door and held it open. As we entered the house, he followed and waited for us inside the front door.

The house was dark and cold, and a musty, damp odor permeated the air. Papers, magazines and other clutter lay in heaps on the table, and so many items were strewn on the floor we had to step over them carefully to avoid falling. Blankets and sheets were piled high on the sofa, and dirty dishes, with clumps of food caked on them, sat in the kitchen sink. That was enough to turn anyone's stomach. "Do you think the house was this way originally," Rose asked me, "or could the police have trashed it?"

"Beats me," I whispered back. "It sure is a pigpen, isn't it? Maybe she lived like this."

As Rose walked around, she recognized things that she knew belonged to Tod and began to gathering them up. Mr. Morgan kept his position at the door, scowling all the time, saying nothing.

Tod had bought Rose and the girls Christmas gifts while he was home in August and had shown them to me for my approval. Amazingly, I found those gifts, wrapped in red and white Christmas paper decorated with gold angels, lying on the living room floor. "She had some nerve." I said, in an angry voice.

Rose looked at me in surprise. "What are you talking about?" Still indignant, I showed her the gifts, which Rose then added to the other things she had collected. I noticed tears glistening on her cheeks as she handled the gaily wrapped boxes, and I wondered if she would ever open them.

I too continued looking for Tod's possessions. Rose, who had gone upstairs, suddenly called for me to come to the second room on the left. When I walked into that room, lo and behold, there was the headboard that belonged to their bed. "How did this girl get the nerve to take furniture that didn't belong to her?" I said, loudly enough for Mr. Morgan to hear me. I shook my head in disgust and went back to the first floor, wandering into a bedroom off the living room. There, lying on the floor, side by side, were Tod's cowboy boots and the sky-blue lamb's wool sweater I had brought him from England. As I stood staring at them, I swore I could feel his presence in that room. I reached down and picked them up, holding them tightly in my arms, biting my lip to keep myself from screaming. I looked around the room and saw that the floor had been torn up and the walls gouged with an ax or other tool. Pieces of clothing, as well as blankets and sheets, were strewn about everywhere. I stood frozen in shock. Suddenly I couldn't breathe and began to gasp for air. Tears streamed down my cheeks as I realized I was in the room where Roger Cline had shot my son. I clenched my fist and started yelling. "Tod, how could they do this to you? You didn't deserve to die this way!"

One of the TEMAC guards heard me and quickly called Rog, who immediately came in and took me by the hand. "Come on, Jan," he said softly, putting his arm around me as he ushered me out of the room and closed the door behind us. I wasn't about to let go of the boots and sweater though; they were coming with me.

Suddenly I felt a strong chill and turned to see Mr. Morgan staring at me. I looked away at once. There was something about him I didn't like at all. He was cold, just like his daughter, devoid of feeling. I wanted to ask him how he could have raised a daughter so conniving and evil. She didn't turn out that way overnight, and I had a feeling that she had been a problem child and a wild teenager. Now she was a murderer too. Perhaps all that had to do with the smoldering rage that glittered like embers in her father's eyes.

Rose found the old-fashioned wash basin and stand Tod had bought her on their first Christmas together, as well as other items he'd bought for her that had special meaning. These she wanted to keep; as for the rest of the furniture and knickknacks, she didn't want any of it, including the headboard. We told the guards they could help themselves or give it to the needy. It was a relief to get out of that house, and I fled back to the car like a horse running from a burning building.

Soon we arrived back in Lewisburg. Jeff was eager to get back to Trish and the baby and Kaitlyn. Rose also needed to be with Elizabeth and Heather. I thanked God they were with us. I don't think I could have made it through that ordeal without them. Rog and I returned to the TEMAC office where, once again, I began going through more papers and files while Rog returned to the accounting books. The phone began ringing. The calls were from local people who had known Tod, and I was amazed how the word had spread that we were in Lewisburg. The callers all had a story about Tod that they wanted to share. I couldn't help but smile as each one told me they were Tod's best friend.

Rog reminded me of our three o'clock appointment with the prosecuting attorney. In the meantime, Carl came back to see if there was anything else he could do for us. He made his way into the office hesitantly and sat down beside me. "Ma'am, I know you have a lot on your mind right now," he said, "but different people have been asking me if you might be planning a memorial service down here for Tod. He had a lot of friends who would like to pay their respects."

I hadn't even thought about a memorial service for Tod in Lewisburg. I told Carl I'd give it some thought and perhaps set a date for a service on our return trip in a week or two. He was delighted and said he would let everyone know.

At 2:30 Rog began loading the Bronco with papers and files. We arrived at the courthouse on time and climbed the stairs to the second floor where Richard Lorensen, or Rick as he was called, was sitting in his office, waiting for us. He stood up as we entered, extending his hand to both of us. I sat down, glancing around his small office. A bookshelf stood behind his desk. A small credenza along another wall showed off family pictures and a framed photo of a grinning golden retriever. With one big leather chair behind Rick's desk and the two large armchairs that we sat in, it made for a tight squeeze.

I couldn't help thinking that this fellow was much too young to be the county prosecutor. I had expected a much older man, at least as old as Rog. But Rick was a handsome young man of about thirty five or younger, dressed nicely in a blue suit and green tie. He was tall and slender, with light brown hair and sparkling blue eyes behind thick glasses that gave him a pensive, scholarly look. Sitting behind his desk, he addressed us in a business-like manner. "I'm truly sorry about your son. I understand you folks talked with Corporal Greene this morning, and therefore you are aware that three people have been arrested for Tod's murder."

"News travels fast in this town," I said. He just grinned.

"Yes, we are aware of three arrests," Rog said. "We'd like to know what the next procedure will be."

Rick explained that they had been appointed counsel by the court, and pretrial hearings would be held before the three actually went to trial. "I've been reading the police reports and have talked with the officers in charge. As you're aware, Tammy Wilson is the one that planned your son's murder. I want to see her in prison for the rest of her life."

"Why shouldn't she get the death penalty?" I said, barely suppressing my rage.

Rick adjusted his glasses and gave me a sympathetic look. "Ma'am, West Virginia doesn't carry the death penalty. All three have lied in their statements, but of the three, Harry Joe Johnson, I think, is the most honest," he said. "I'm considering offering him a plea bargain to testify against Tammy Wilson and Roger Cline."

I moved to the edge of my chair, sensing a red flag go up. "Why? He's just as guilty as the other two. Why should he get a lesser sentence?" I said through clenched teeth.

"You're right," Rick said, "he is just as guilty, but I'm after the person who is really responsible for your son's murder, and that is Tammy Wilson. She has no feelings for anyone or anything, and she planned the crime. She's a danger to everyone."

"Mr. Lorensen," I said slowly, "I talked with that woman a dozen times a day when Tod was supposed to be missing, and she knew he was dead. I know what kind of a person she is. Nothing would please me more than to see her locked up and the key thrown away."

Rick looked at me intently for a moment. "Mrs. McQuaid, would you be willing to testify?" he asked.

"I'll do anything to see her convicted for life," I replied.

Rick asked that I write down all the conversations Tammy Wilson and I had had. That was going to be easy, since I practically knew them by heart and was more than willing to compile the list. They would be ready for him on our next visit to Lewisburg. Rick mentioned that there was a good possibility he would also call Rog as a witness.

To be sure we would be notified about updated information, Rick suggested that we give our address to his secretary. Then, glancing at his watch, he apologized for the short time he spent with us, but he was scheduled for another meeting. "It's been a pleasure meeting both of you," he said, "I'm sorry it was under these unfortunate circumstances."

We left Rick Lorensen's office and headed toward Charleston, two hours away. The mountain roads were as winding as a roller coaster track. They made the drive tedious, if not dangerous, and the Bronco was not the most comfortable vehicle. The ride seemed to last forever. When we arrived, we found that we had a little more than an hour before we had to be at the funeral home. We found a nice, little quiet restaurant, but nothing on the menu appealed to me. I had a nervous stomach and didn't feel like eating. I ordered a chef salad but didn't eat much of it. I kept looking at my watch as I pushed the food around on my plate like a bored child.

"Is that all you're going to eat?" Rog asked, frowning.

"You're acting like my mother," I snapped. "I'm not hungry."

"I don't mean to act like your mother, but I'm concerned about you."

I sighed and patted his shoulder. "Thanks, but I just can't eat anymore." Glancing at my watch again, I exclaimed, "Look at the time! We need to get going." We got into the Bronco, and although Rog had directions to the funeral home, he took out the Charleston map and scanned it carefully, engineer that he was.

A few minutes later, we arrived at the funeral home, which was located on a side street in Charleston. The street was dark and dreary, barely lit with dull street lights. The building itself was made of dark, red brick; a small light revealed a small sign that read *Baker's Funeral Home, Jack Baker Funeral Director.* Rog parked right in front of the building. I didn't want to go in and sat still while Rog climbed out of the Bronco. He walked around and opened the door for me, but I didn't budge.

"Aren't you coming?" he asked, as he held out his hand to help me out. The moment I dreaded had arrived. I didn't want this to be for real. I wanted my son alive. I wanted to see his smile and hear the laughter in his voice when he said, "You're the best, Mom."

"Come on, Jan," Rog said softly, taking my hand in his as I slowly stepped onto the sidewalk. We continued holding hands as we walked in the front door. It was quiet, dark, and eerie, as most funeral homes seem to be. The air smelled like a strange blend of pine needles and mothballs. There wasn't anyone around. A signal must have sounded somewhere when we walked in because a side door opened and the funeral director appeared. He introduced himself and explained that he would return in about fifteen minutes. He escorted us to an area where we could wait, then disappeared back through the side door like a solemn ghost.

Rog appeared to be calm, but suddenly he began pacing, which belied his serene demeanor. I took a seat and picked up a news magazine, flipping pages, not reading, or even looking at the pictures. The wait was nerve-wracking. Once again the side door opened and the funeral director appeared. Walking over to Rog with his back to me, he handed Rog something, whispered a few words, then turned and, once again, vanished through the side door. *What is this?* I thought. *A funeral home or the Starship Enterprise?*

Rog continued standing with his back to me, so I couldn't see what he was looking at. Suddenly, he began sobbing. I rushed over to him and laid my hand on his shoulder. "What did he give you?" I asked. He just shook his head as I watched him slip a small envelope into his jacket pocket. "Tell me, what did he give you?" I asked again. He couldn't answer me, so after a few moments, I tried again. "Rog, please tell me what he gave you that has made you so unhappy."

He walked over and sat down in a chair, resting his head in his hands. I sat down next to him. Throughout the past weeks, Rog had had his moments, but whatever it was he just received, it had torn him apart.

"It's okay, I can wait until you're ready to talk about it," I said, relenting.

He was so choked up, he could hardly speak, but at last he managed a few soft words. "He gave me the neck chains Tod was wearing. I don't want you to see them now." He took out his handkerchief out of his pocket and dabbed at his eyes.

"Why not?"

"Because one .... Please, let's drop it," he said, his voice cracking dreadfully.

I couldn't stand it any more. "Oh, Rog! Please! You must tell me."

"Because ... one is covered with blood," he said, continuing to cradle his head in his hands.

I stopped asking. Instead I returned to the magazines, desperately trying to distract myself from the terrible image that Rog's words had painted in my mind. Within minutes the funeral director appeared again, this time carrying a square, black box. I stood up and walked over to meet him, and he handed me the plastic box, textured to look like wood. I held it close to my breast. It was still warm. I knew that I was holding my son, and I knew that it would be the last time I would ever put my arms around him. "Dear God, how can this be my son?" I cried. "It's not supposed to be this way." Rog reached over to take the box from me, but I screamed at him, "No!"

Holding the box tightly, my thoughts drifted back to the moment when the nurse handed Tod to me for the very first time in the hospital. He was wrapped snugly in a little blue blanket, and the corner of the blanket covered his tiny face. As I lifted the corner of the blanket and looked at my baby son, I couldn't believe I had just given birth to this miracle from God. He was sleeping peacefully and looked very content. He was the most beautiful baby in the world. I held him close to my breast, loving him, and kissed his tender cheek as I held his tiny fingers, whispering softly, "Oh, how I love you."

Thirty-five years later, I was holding him again, but this time he was in a warm, black box. My love was just as strong as it was the day he was born, but I couldn't kiss his cheek or touch his fingers. All I could do was grip the box and gaze at Rog through my uncontrollable tears. "This is not the way I wanted to get our son back." Rog wrapped his arms around me, and together we clasped Tod between us, weeping in silent suffering. The funeral director quietly slipped back through the side door.

Every mother who has ever lost a child must have felt the horrible heartache and pain I was feeling at that moment. I looked down at the box and whispered softly, "Remember, I love you. You will never leave my heart!"

# CHAPTER NINE

As we stood holding the box between us, a sweet fragrance of flowers from another room permeated the funeral home. The odor was making me sick to my stomach, but I didn't want to let go of the box. I didn't want to give him up. How could I ever accept the fact that he was gone?

In time, Rog and I quietly exited the building. As we approached the Bronco, Rog took the box from me and placed it in the back of the car with the rest of the luggage. I wondered why he hadn't placed it on the back seat, closer to us. I should have spoken up, but I didn't have any gumption left in me.

It was a silent ride back to Pittsburgh. The dark mountain roads were dreary, lined with trees shedding their leaves. I began sinking deeper and deeper into depression and felt guilty that Tod's remains were in the back, like cargo. I wondered how much more trauma I could possibly handle. Rog and I talked very little, and when we spoke our conversations were short. Perhaps I was still resenting the fact Tod was cremated. On the dark mountain road, with nothing to look at, I found myself dozing off.

"Jan, this has been an extremely taxing day for both of us," Rog said. "I don't have to see how stressed you are, I can feel it a mile away."

Rog's words broke a dam inside of me and suddenly I was wide awake. My anger and frustration poured out of me like a raging river. "Yes, I'm stressed. I'd give up everything I own to have my son alive. I want to be able to give him the cookies I promised him and share with him the gold medal I won in Salt Lake City, and I can't do that because that bitch and her cronies killed him. And, yes, they're behind bars, but Tod is gone forever. On top of that, you put him in the back like ... like a suitcase!"

Rog was silent for a few moments. "I honestly didn't think about it that way, and I'm sorry." With that he pulled over to the side of the road and moved the small back box to the back seat. I mumbled a thank you, and Rog got back into the Bronco. "Jan, you're tighter than a drum. Why don't you try and catch a little sleep?"

I was exhausted, but I was afraid to fall asleep lest Rog imitate me. "I don't want you falling asleep behind the wheel. You're stressed too, except you keep your tension bottled up inside."

"I'm doing fine," he said, assuring me. "So close your eyes." He gave me his gentle grin.

At some point I must have taken his advice and drifted off to sleep. The next thing I knew it was 3:00 A.M. and we were back in Aspinwall. The house was dark except for the back porch light. "Let's go in. I'll unload the car in the morning," Rog said.

"What about Tod?" I asked.

"I don't think it would be wise to bring the box into the house," he murmured. "The girls are suffering enough without seeing this. Besides," he said with a smile, "Tod was an outdoor guy. He never minded sleeping in the car."

We entered the house, trying to be as quiet as possible so as not to wake anyone. I didn't realize how weary and worn out I was until I climbed into bed. For the first time in weeks, it felt good to lie down, and I dozed off in seconds. I wasn't sure how long I had been sleeping when I felt a kiss on my cheek. I tried desperately to open my eyes. There stood Heather leaning over me, gazing at me with her big, brown eyes and smiling broadly. "Good morning, Nanny. I missed you," she whispered in my ear.

I had no idea what time it was because I couldn't get my eyes open wide enough to read the clock. I just knew it was still dark outside. I threw back the covers so Heather could slide in beside me, then I kissed her cheek and gave her a squeeze. "I missed you too," I whispered. "Let's try and go back to sleep for another hour or two, okay?"

As she snuggled down beside me to get comfortable, she looked up at me and whispered, "I love you, Nanny."

"And I love you." She soon drifted back to sleep. What an angel!

How lucky we were to have Elizabeth and Heather with us, I thought. Children have a way of healing hearts with their love.

The pungent smell of coffee and the chatter of voices woke me the second time. Heather was gone, and so was Rog, though I had never felt either of them leave. When I arrived in the kitchen, it was full of family, and everyone was talking at once. I looked around for Rog and found him on the phone. There was so much noise in the kitchen I headed for the living room for some peace and quiet. Rog waved a piece of paper at me, which said, *11:00 at the funeral home.* I nodded. I sat down and was just getting comfortable when Mom McQuaid and my sisters-in-law, Jan and Carolyn, came in to join me. "Rose told us a little bit about the trip," Carolyn said. "I'm sorry it was so horrible."

Mom, who was sitting next to me, put her arm around me. "I can only imagine what it must have been like for you," she said.

I couldn't help but hug my sisters-in-laws. I thanked God for being so blessed as to have them, as well as Mom McQuaid. Rog got off the phone and came in to give me a good-morning kiss. "Are you feeling any better this morning?" he asked

"I was so out of it," I replied, "I didn't even have one of my horror nightmares." Just then the phone rang. "That's my mom," I yelled. "I'd know that ring anywhere." Everyone laughed as I went to answer it. My mom was happy to hear my voice, and began asking about the trip. I didn't want to discuss it, however, so she went on to tell me not to worry, that everything had been taken care of at the cemetery and the family had been notified.

Rog motioned to me as he pointed to his watch. I cut my mom short and thanked her for all her help. At 10:30 Rog and I left for the funeral home. Tom, the director, greeted us at the door, and we followed him into his office. He and Rog began discussing the funeral arrangements as I sat and listened, my stomach tying itself into a knot, my fists clenching so hard that I thought my hands would break. Reality began setting in. I didn't want to accept Tod's burial; that would make his death final. Rog went out to the Bronco, brought in the black box, and handed it to Tom, who gently held it as he carried it out of the room. I just couldn't bring myself to believe that Tod was in that box. My mind began to wander, thinking about

Tammy Wilson, Roger Cline, and Harry Joe Johnson in a prison cell. All three were exactly where they deserved to be.

The day of the funeral dawned dreary and damp as I woke and headed for the kitchen. The door into the kitchen was closed, but I was able to see the light shining from underneath. Walking down the hall, I smelled the wonderful aroma of hazelnut coffee, my very favorite. I entered the kitchen to find Mom having breakfast. The table was set with her homemade sour cream coffee cake, and flaky French crescent rolls were neatly placed on a plate, ready for the morning crowd. Pouring myself a cup of coffee, I sat down beside her. I felt as low as one could get and, perhaps, even lower than that, if such a thing were possible. I told her that I didn't know how I could make it through that day.

She smiled sadly and took my hand. "Honey, if I could, I would do anything to make this all easier for you," she said. "But I don't know how. Tod's my firstborn grandchild, and I'm in agony over his death. I don't have enough words to begin to tell you how much I'm going to miss him." Her eyes welled up with tears.

I excused myself and went down into the basement. There I found an old kitchen chair and sat down and wept. I didn't want to be a part of this day. I didn't want to bury my son. Anger and hate boiled inside me at those three animals who had taken Tod's life. I wanted them dead, too. I wanted their parents to suffer as I was suffering.

I began hearing more footsteps and voices in the kitchen as people were starting to rise. I wanted to avoid everyone, and most of all, conversation. It took some doing, but I was finally able to sneak up to the second floor without being noticed. I sat down on the chair by the front bedroom window, watching the street traffic. Then I heard the bedroom door open and turned around to see Rose peeking in. "Just checking up on you," she said, her sweet smile marred by the weariness in her face.

I invited her in and we talked for a while, about everything except the funeral, and I realized that she was trying to divert my thoughts from that terrible event. I was happy for our short time together. Glancing at the clock, I knew Jeff would soon be arriving, and I had to hurry. Rose left and I found myself flustered, walking around in circles, looking for articles of clothing and jewelry. I couldn't remember where I had hung the jacket I wanted to wear or where I had left my watch. Finally, with Rog's help, I was ready just before Jeff arrived at 9:15. We had to stop along the way for my mother, who was anxiously waiting at her door.

It was a somber ride. I began to pray silently.

Tom was standing in the parking lot waiting for us and directed us to line up behind the hearse. I lowered my head as tears began streaming down my face. I couldn't bear the thought of my son being in that hearse. This was all wrong. Children were supposed to outlive their parents. Little girls were supposed to play and laugh with their loving daddy, and life was supposed to be full and complete. None of that was true any longer.

As soon as the rest of the family arrived and Tom lined up their cars in the cortege, the procession began. It had been six years since we had taken this route to bury my dad. Tod would now be joining him. It was all so final, like a door slamming shut forever. My brain was numb, and I stood frozen at the graveside. I don't remember much, except seeing Rose kneel to the ground sobbing, with Elizabeth and Heather clinging to her coat, shedding the tears of their broken hearts. My body shook as my own tears streamed down my face. It was only when Jeff took hold of my arm and softly whispered, "Come on, Mom," and started walking me back to the car that I realized it was over. My Tod was gone forever.

I watched as Rog strode over to a nearby oak tree and pounded it with his fist. Long, loud sobs racked his body. Rog's wild behavior was completely unlike him, and his outburst frightened me. Jeff helped my mother and me into the car, then walked back to help his dad, but Rog had walked to the graveside and sat down on the ground, still sobbing. Weeks of emotions held in check had finally broken loose. Jeff helped him up and led him toward the car. As he climbed inside, I could see that his face was filled with rage. I had never seen him so angry before, and I was afraid he would work himself into a heart attack. Jeff reassured my worried mom that Rog needed to release his tension and that he would be fine.

By the time we reached the church, Rog had calmed down, and I thought he might make it through the memorial service after all.

He took my arm, and Jeff helped his grandmother as we entered the church and walked to the first pew where Rose and the girls were sitting quietly with Mom and Dad McQuaid. I eased down next to Elizabeth as Heather sat on Rose's lap, where she hid her face in her mother's shoulder and cried. Rose tried to comfort her, in spite of her own sorrow. Elizabeth looked up at me through her tears. "Nanny, I loved my daddy," she whispered. "I'll miss him something awful."

I held her close. "Always remember the fun times you had with him, but the most important thing to remember is how much he loved you and Heather."

It was a beautiful service. Tod's favorite hymn was sung, and Mike's eulogy was on right on target. He spoke of his own memories of Tod, of playing bumper pool and Mouse Trap with him. He said that Tod seemed to take on the responsibility of caring for the rest of the cousins and caring for the grandparents and all the rest of the family. Once, when Tod learned of a cousin who had gotten into some mischief, he jumped into his car and drove to the home of that cousin and talked to him, trying to encourage him to get back on the straight and narrow. Tod always seemed to be looking out for someone else, he said, especially Rose and his two daughters. Mike spoke of Tod's business and employees and the fact that Tod was always looking out for others.

"His death seems to be far from fair," Mike said. "Tod fought evil; consequently, he was put into closer contact with evil. Now it seems as if evil has prevailed. But we, as the people of God, have a different view of life. Death is not the final word. God promises eternal life to his people. Life cannot be snuffed out by any person or any power in this world. Furthermore, it appears that some, if not all, of the truth has begun to surface around Tod's death. Thankfully we can live with the knowledge that God's justice will ultimately prevail against evil, that the God of light has already conquered it."

Several times Mike paused, but he managed to get through the eulogy. I was proud of him, and I know that Bob and Jan felt great pride in their son. In my heart, I knew Tod was looking down on us with his wonderful smile.

When we returned home, everyone gathered around the dining room table, chattering about their plans for leaving the next morning. Rog and I were extending our stay a few extra days, making sure the folks were okay, and spending some time with Jeff, Trish, Kaitlyn, and baby Tierney.

The days passed quickly, and we were soon on our way back to New Jersey. When we arrived home, I hesitated before going inside the house. It meant reliving the torment of what I went through before going to Pittsburgh. I sat on the front porch steps and watched a few birds in the grass as they hunted for insects, then flew into the large oak tree. I pictured Tod as a teenager lying on the ground with his camera, taking pictures from every possible angle of that tree until he had taken the four seasons of the oak tree he loved and claimed as his. I glanced at the window boxes on our two front windows that he and Jeff had painted and filled with bright red geraniums as a welcome home when Rog and I returned from a trip. Such wonderful memories! My trance was broken when the front door opened.

"Aren't you coming in?" Rog asked.

"Yes, I'm just sitting here reminiscing." I slowly got up and entered the house. Rose and the girls were upstairs. I heard laughter and the sound of little feet running around. I went straight to our bedroom and sat on the edge of our bed, staring at the phone on my nightstand, the phone I had used to call Tammy Wilson. The phone I had used to listen to all the lies she had told me. Slowly, I began to reconstruct all the conversations we had had. To think Tod had already been dead and she had known it. In my entire life I had never met or encountered anyone so heartless and ruthless.

I was worn out and didn't want to talk to anyone. I needed time alone. Bed was becoming my favorite place to escape. Rog made a few phone calls to some of our friends, letting them know we were home, and of course, the main topic was Tod. Eventually, Rog came in and sat on the edge of the bed as he began sharing the conversations he had had. He mentioned that everyone wanted to know when there would be a memorial service for Tod.

"Why another service?" I asked. I wasn't sure I could handle another service. Pittsburgh was our home, and it was where all our family lived, as well as our many friends. Rog felt New Jersey had been our home for twenty-seven years. We had many friends there too, and he was right.

We had been members of St. John's Lutheran Church in Summit since Tod was nine years old. He attended Sunday school there, was an active youth member, sang in the junior choir, was confirmed there. It was the church where he and Rose were married. In spite of all that, I still dreaded the idea of having to go through another memorial service. Our good friend Duane offered to help take care of most of the arrangements that had to be made. Calls were made to the men's barbershop choruses and Sweet Adeline chapters, as well as St. John's members and our other friends. Rose took care of notifying all their friends.

When the day of the service came, the church was not only filled with friends we hadn't seen in some time, but was positively overflowing with Barbershoppers and Sweet Adelines. Tod had a love for barbershop music and had been a member of the Westfield Barbershop Chorus. It was a hobby he and Rog shared. The sound of harmony that rang in the church that morning was awesome. Tod would have loved it.

The next few days I did nothing but think of Tod. Rose went back to work, and the girls attended school. The phone stopped ringing because our friends stopped calling. Rog was spending more time in front of the computer. Our mail was overflowing with sympathy cards and Mass cards and personal notes. I read them all over and over, thinking how lucky we were to have so many wonderful, caring friends and to have prayers said for Tod.

One morning, thinking over all that had happened, I recalled Tod's neck chains that the funeral director had given to Rog. He explained he had given them to Rose to take to her brother's jewelry store to be cleaned. The silver chain had to be disposed of. I was hurt that he hadn't told me what they had done.

"I'm sorry," Rog said. "It was a decision Rose and I made because we felt you didn't need something else added to your sorrow. We did what we felt was best for you."

Within three days, Rose handed me a small envelope. Inside was Tod's gold chain; it looked like new. As I gazed at the glittering chain, I thought of Elizabeth and Heather. The three of them were all that I had that was a part of Tod.

Rog took me by surprise when he asked to wear the chain. He

was one not to wear jewelry, other than his wedding ring. He was mourning Tod in his own way, and I think he felt that, by wearing the chain, it would make him feel closer to his son. Rose hooked the chain around his neck as he kept taking deep breaths. Without saying a word, he turned and walked into the computer room.

One evening at dinner, Rog mentioned we should be making a trip to Lewisburg to check on the business. His early retirement from AT&T and my leaving the travel business made it easier to go to Lewisburg during the week, while the girls were in school all day. Rog would now be handling TEMAC. He had helped Tod to install an alarm system in our home and, as an electrical engineer, was quite knowledgeable. I made him promise that he would not take on any new clients, especially since I was pushing him to sell the business.

I was to have a list of Tammy Wilson's conversations ready for the prosecutor when we returned to Lewisburg, but writing them down was not easy. It wasn't that I couldn't remember them; it just hurt so much to remember them. Nevertheless I wrote them down, taking my time, trying to recall every detail, every word, reliving all those lies. I knew it was important to have a record of those calls.

Late in the afternoon the following Sunday, we left for Lewisburg. It was a long, ten-hour, uneventful drive, and we were both glad to enter our motel room, where we collapsed on the bed.

The next morning I stood in the middle of the TEMAC office, wondering where to begin. Before Rog had had a chance to call Carl, he arrived. Carl gave Rog the names of Tod's insurance agent, as well as the TEMAC attorney. Making an appointment with Tim, the TEMAC attorney, Rog asked him if he knew about a will Tod might have had, only to be told that he had never handled a will for Tod. While Rog was busy with the business, I continued placing office papers in the "round file," hoping to come across a will Tod might have hidden somewhere.

Looking at the top of the file cabinet, I shuddered, seeing papers piled on top once more. Removing everything again, I sat at the desk and began going through all the papers one by one. Inside the file cabinet were even more outdated documents. As I began going through the files, I couldn't help but smile. Tod was like his father: he saved everything. I came across the files of current employee applications and pulled them out. Sitting at the desk, I began reading. When I came across Tammy Wilson's employment application, I noticed that it wasn't completely filled out. If Tod had questioned her about the missing information, I'm sure she had a story to back up all her claims. She always had a story, an explanation, an excuse, a lie. One account rang uncomfortably true: records of high scores in the gun shooting classes she had taken in the army.

Harry Joe Johnson's application stated that he graduated from high school and went directly into the Navy. His discharge papers stapled to his application indicated that he had been released due to stress. If Roger Cline had filled out an application, it was missing.

While I was busy reading about the TEMAC employees, Rog made a trip to the bank to check on Tod's accounts and have them temporarily frozen. Even though Tammy was in jail, he wasn't leaving anything to chance.

At 3:15 P.M. we headed to the courthouse for our appointment with County Prosecutor Rick Lorensen. Once again, he seemed to be on a tight schedule and wasted no time in getting down to business. I handed him my written report of conversations with Tammy Wilson, and he quickly glanced over them. He told us that Harry Joe Johnson had gone before a grand jury and was charged with first-degree murder, but he had agreed to plea bargain and testify against Tammy Wilson and Roger Cline. Rick said that he had accepted the plea bargain. "As I explained to you before," Rick said, "I felt that he's the most truthful of the three."

He knew I was against this position, but it was obvious it didn't matter to him what I thought. He was the prosecutor and was going to do as he saw fit. "What if he doesn't come through and lies?" I asked.

"If he doesn't tell the truth, he would be charged with a felony offense of perjury."

"Just what kind of sentence will he receive for this plea bargaining?" I could feel my face begin to burn with anger. Rick said the most probably sentence was a maximum of not less than five years nor more than eighteen years in prison. "Five to eighteen years? Is that all he would have to serve for taking part in my son's murder?" I said, aghast. "I'm sorry, I don't agree with that at all." I glared at Rick, but he disarmed me with a weary smile.

**Jeff & Tod**

**The wild goose chase begins at Meadow Bridge**

**Murder Scene**

**Courthouse**

**TEMAC Office**

Tod loves Rose

Tod — days before
his disappearance

Heather, Tod, & Elizabeth

Jan McQuaid
"You're the best, Mom."

Tod's presence
is always with his family.

"Mrs. McQuaid, sometimes you have to lose to win. I want to get the person who is really responsible for your son's death. Tammy Wilson lied to you, she lied to the police, and her statements have been inconsistent all along. She needs to be behind bars for the rest of her life."

Before I could say anything else, Rog interrupted. "You have to do what you think is right. Whatever it takes to put Wilson in prison for life, I'm for it. However you have to do it, that's what we want you to do," he said.

I glared at him, gritting my teeth. I couldn't believe he had said that. "All three should be behind bars forever, not just Wilson," I said adamantly.

Rick looked down at his desk calendar. "Folks, April 24th, 1991, is the court date set for the trial of Harry Joe Johnson. You'll receive official notification of the trial in a week or two. A plea bargain is a trial without a jury, and Judge Jolliffe will be presiding." The name didn't mean anything to us. "By the way, there is a possibility of a change of venue for Tammy Wilson."

"Why?" Rog asked.

"Her lawyer feels she wouldn't get a fair trial here in Lewisburg because too many people know her. It will probably be held in Morgantown instead."

When we arrived back at the TEMAC office, I was not in the best of moods. I never agreed with the plea bargain for Harry Joe, and thought that Rick was just making the situation easier on himself, since now he would not have to prepare for three murder trials.

*What a mess!* I thought, surveying the office. It was depressing to think that Tammy could make a complete shambles of the place in eighteen days. I had cleaned the bathrooms but hadn't even begun to tackle the kitchen, with its dirty sink and dishes. Worse yet, when I opened the refrigerator I found food with green mold growing on it. I put on rubber gloves and, with one large garbage bag, emptied out the entire refrigerator. Rog continued working on the accounting. It seems Tammy had made a mess of that too.

Rog mentioned to Carl that he wanted to start looking for

someone to run the office and do payroll in his absence, and Carl recommended a woman he knew with bookkeeping experience. Rog called her, and she arrived the next morning for an interview. After Lottie and Rog talked, he was so impressed with her that he offered her the job on the spot. Rog brought her into the kitchen where I was still cleaning. He made the introductions and she hugged me, saying how sorry she was about Tod. She had seen him around town but didn't know him personally. "Oh, Mrs. McQuaid," she said, "you should be glad Judge Jolliffe is going to be the trial judge. He's known as the 'Hanging Judge,' and you can be sure that those rats will get what's coming to them."

I wasn't surprised to find out that Lottie knew about Judge Jolliffe. Carl had told me earlier that "Everyone in Lewisberg knows what's going on with whom, when, and where. You can't keep a secret here." Lottie and I had a short conversation, and my instincts told me she was kind, sincere, and down-to-earth.

Arriving on time at 9:30 A.M. the next morning, Lottie joined Rog, who was already working on the books. For me, it was another day of cleaning and answering the phone. Carl stopped in from time to time just to check on how things were going, and he and Lottie shared stories about the latest gossip in their West Virginia twang. I laughed out at their tales, the first time in weeks. One day Carl asked me if I had given any thought to a local memorial service. In fact, I had.

Tod had been a charter member and past president of the Men of the Greenbrier Barbershop Chorus. He also had donated and installed a security system in Carnegie Hall, where the chorus held their annual shows. I wanted to hold the service there and have the barbershop chorus sing. Since there weren't any Lutheran churches in the area, Tod didn't have an affiliation anywhere, but I planned on asking around to help locate a pastor for the service. Carl agreed to help.

The next morning I answered the phone in between making what seemed like a hundred calls. With the help of Tod's friends, all my plans were falling into place. I received a call from a local minister, saying he had penciled in the date, and we would meet and discuss the service on our return trip. I was overwhelmed at the generosity of the people in Lewisburg. I just wondered how I would have the strength to get thought yet another memorial service for my wonderful son.

A few days later Rog and I went to visit the TEMAC attorney, Tim, after dinner. Arriving on time at his huge Georgian-style house, we met Tim at the door and he ushered us into his office just off the wide-open foyer of his beautiful home. All I could think of was *Gone with the Wind*. The chairs and other pieces of furniture were reproductions of antiques, and a beautiful fireplace graced one wood-paneled wall. My gaze was immediately drawn to the window treatment of hunter green drapes with a pattern of brown hunting dogs that gave the room a stylish, masculine look. The entire wall behind his desk was a beautiful, walnut bookcase filled with law books. I was impressed with fact that all the papers were neatly stacked and well organized.

Tim's large frame fit well in his burgundy leather desk chair. His desk gleamed like a polished gem. Before we got down to talking business, Tim talked about his friendship with Tod. He went on to discuss what kind of affairs he handled for the TEMAC business, again explaining that he didn't know if Tod had a will. It was something they had never discussed.

Rog asked Tim to continue handling any legal problems that TEMAC might encounter, and told the lawyer that he was unsure what to do next. Tim wrote down a to-do list for Rog. Looking over what had to be done and the time involved, Rog decided to work from home. This implied to me that it would be a while before we could sell the business.

It was a grueling ten-hour drive home. As we opened the door, the girl's joyous greeting, complete with sloppy kisses and hugs, made my day. After a while, Rog went to check his e-mail, the girls left to watch television, and Rose and I went into the kitchen to talk by ourselves.

"You look awfully tired," she said, giving me a meaningful look. I told her that I hadn't been sleeping well, that nightmares woke me up every hour on the hour. "What kind of nightmares?" Rose asked.

I told her about the dream I'd had the night before and several times before that. I was running to escape someone chasing me, but

I didn't know who it was. Although I was running as fast as I could, I couldn't get away. I ran down an alleyway, and there was Tod on the ground with someone pointing a gun at him. The gunman and I struggled, but he and the guy chasing me kept overpowering me. My heart was pounding so hard and fast that it woke me up. I was soaking wet. "Worse yet, I keep asking myself questions, like, was it really Tod we buried? What if Tod is alive, stumbling around somewhere with a loss of memory? If I could have just touched his hair or seen his hand, then I would have known for sure."

"Jan, you have to get rid of those ideas," Rose said, sadly shaking her head. "The dental records proved it was Tod. For your own health, you must come to terms and face the fact, like the rest of us, that Tod is gone."

I couldn't help myself; I broke into a sob, jumped up and hurried out of the room. Yes, Tod was probably gone, I knew. But in my mind a tiny spark of hope still glimmered: What if he were alive? I couldn't let it go!

# CHAPTER TEN

In the weeks that followed, Rog spent a lot of time buried in the computer with the TEMAC business. Doubts and questions still spun about in my mind like leaves in a whirlwind. Why didn't Tod see Tammy for what she was? Why didn't he avoid her? If she drugged him, what did she give him? Did he realize what was happening to him? Did he put up a fight? What were his last hours like? I could only imagine how awful it must have been for him.

These questions devoured me every day. When I approached Rog to discuss them, he found excuses to avoid me, saying he was too busy to talk. He wasn't interested talking about Tod's death, and he didn't seem concerned about my feelings. How I needed him to give me some tender loving care, but that wasn't happening. He was changing; TEMAC was becoming his top priority. He seemed to be at the computer from sunup to sundown. We didn't hear from our friends, and I was beginning to feel forgotten. I began to realize that people have a tendency to abandon friends after a death. When a loved one dies, friends and family members are there for them during the wake, but when the funeral is over, everyone is gone and you're alone. That's when the reality of death hits the hardest, and when friends and family are needed the most. Still, all too often there is no one to talk to. I thanked God for my friend Sharon's long, frequent phone calls from Florida. I only wished she were able to sit and be with me, take my hand and assure me that I was acting normally, considering the circumstances.

With Elizabeth in first grade and Heather attending pre-school, I wasn't needed as much for child care. As a result, I dwelled on Tod's murder and sank deeper and deeper into depression. Sleeping became my favorite escape from reality. At least when I was sleeping I didn't have to think about anything, especially Tod's death. I was developing a terrible apathy toward almost everything. Listening to music no longer interested me, and I couldn't care less about gardening or shopping. When I wasn't sleeping, I lay propped up in bed, staring at the TV. Games shows, courtroom shows, soaps, even cartoons — they all seemed alike to me. The housework piled up, but I didn't care.

The situation became so serious that Rog even began doing laundry from time to time. Rose came home from work and dug in to do whatever had to be done, including dinner preparations, while I just existed. The evil nature of Tammy Wilson had changed my life, sucked my joy right out of me. The only thing that I still made time for was being with Elizabeth and Heather. In the evening they romped into the bedroom full of energy, their faces glowing with exuberance as they jumped up on the bed, bringing books for me to read to them. One evening as they sat on our bed, Heather asked, "Nanny, are you sad about my daddy?"

"Yes, very sad," I answered.

"Can he call us on the telephone from Heaven?" she asked.

"No, I'm afraid he can't, but I believe he's watching over you."

"Can he see us?" Elizabeth asked.

"I'm not sure," I said carefully, not wanting to crush her hopes. "Perhaps if you look in the sky and see a bright star twinkling, it could be your daddy's way of telling you, 'Here I am, shining brightly, watching over you.' "

"Really?" Elizabeth looked at me, puzzled. "How do you know that?"

I laughed softly. "Well, when my daddy died, one night my mom walked into the backyard and looked up at the night sky. There were lots of stars, but there was only one big bright star in the sky, and she felt in her heart it was my daddy telling her he was watching over us."

"When I say my prayers, can I look for a bright star?" Elizabeth asked eagerly. "If I think it's Daddy, can I talk to him?"

"You certainly can," I answered. *Thank God for a child's imagina-*

*tion,* I thought. It buffered the pain.

The evening arrived when I had to begin packing for our trip to Lewisburg. Elizabeth and Heather came in and climbed on the bed as they watched me stuff clothes in a suitcase, their little faces creased with frowns. They were unhappy with us leaving them again. We talked for a while, and after I hugged and kissed them, they were off. I continued packing, and Rog came in.

"Are you ready to go?" he asked.

"As ready as I'm going to be. Of course, my preference would be to stay home," I said.

Either Rog pretended not to hear me, or he really didn't hear me. "I'd like to get an early start in the morning," he said, "so I suggest you get a good night's sleep." The warmth I once took for granted was no longer in his voice or manner, and I felt myself beginning to resent his presence.

We arrived in Lewisburg late in the afternoon, and after checking into the Fort Savannah Motel, we headed for the TEMAC office. Rog immediately began making phone calls, first to Carl, then to Lottie, letting them know we had arrived.

The next morning I began making phone calls in final preparations for the memorial service. I was so busy on the phone that I never noticed the top of the file cabinet. Then, as I happened to glance that way, I couldn't believe it: Once again, the top of the cabinet was covered with papers. I was annoyed with whoever was putting things there instead of throwing them away or filing them. Finishing my phone calls, I was tempted to take everything off the cabinet and just dump it, but on second thought I began going through the stack piece by piece. As I reached the bottom of the pile, I came across a sealed envelope. Turning it over I was stunned to read, in Tod's handwriting, *'LAST WILL AND TESTAMENT OF TOD E. MCQUAID TO BE OPENED ONLY BY THE TEMAC LAWYER.'*

Where did it come from? Who put it there? Someone had it in their possession and knew I would clean off the top of that file cabinet once I saw the clutter. Was it Carl? The envelope had not been opened or tampered with. I leaped from the chair and began yelling for Rog, who came running down the hall. "Look what I found on top of the filing cabinet," I said, handing him the envelope, but he didn't seem as surprised as I was. "Who do you think put it there?"

"It doesn't matter. What's important is that now we have it," he said. "Thank God it wasn't in the hands of Tammy Wilson."

Rog immediately called Tim, making an appointment for late that afternoon.

Because of the excitement of finding the will, I had forgotten the appointment I had made with the minister, and he arrived at the office later than I expected. I had to apologize for our short visit, due to our unexpected appointment with the attorney. I thanked him for his willingness to conduct the memorial service, especially since our son wasn't a member of his congregation. Before leaving, he held my hand as we prayed.

Rog and I made the short trip to Tim's office in tense silence. It was nice being able to once again enjoy the reassuringly masculine decor of that office and the comfortable furniture. Opening Tod's will, Tim glanced over it and assured us that it was a legal will. As he began reading it, Rog and I both began crying. Tod's will included a personal message to all his family members. The heartbreaker was his expression of love for all of us, especially Elizabeth and Heather. Given the lies that Tammy had told everyone about her so-called relationship with Tod, nothing would have delighted me more than to read her the message Tod had written to Rose: "I'm sorry we parted. You will always be my wife."

We thanked Tim and headed back to the office. I was feeling very blue and wanted to go home. I couldn't bear to look out of the office window, with its view of the courthouse and county jail, so I stayed in the bedroom with the door closed. Rog began making calls to clients while I sank deeper into darkness and resentment. I wanted the TEMAC business to be sold, but Rog had other ideas. Although someone had offered to buy TEMAC's alarm accounts, Rog turned them down. Nothing I said or felt could change his mind. He didn't want to give up TEMAC.

The next day I buried myself in a 500-page historical romance. Whenever Rog asked me if I were okay, which was often, I would answer him with a brief nod. As he began gathering equipment in preparation to go out and take care of a few alarm problems, he asked me to come along, but I just shook my head.

"Oh, come on," he said. "It might be fun."

I closed my book with a thump. "Fun? It's a nightmare. Why you turned down that offer is beyond me," I said, my voice rising with each word.

Rog stared at me as if he just stepped into a nest of rattlesnakes. "The price wasn't right. I can't give TEMAC away."

I snorted and shook my paperback at him. "The price will never be right! People down here don't have the money to pay your asking price. Can't you see that this business is tearing us apart?"

He frowned, then turned and stalked out the front door. I was so angry my heart was pounding. Why was my good, sweet husband being so stubborn?

At five o'clock Rog returned. As we were getting ready to lock up and go back to the motel, Jeff walked in. "What a nice surprise," I cried, giving him a hug and kiss on the cheek. He had driven down from Pittsburgh to have dinner with us and attend the memorial service. For a change of pace, we went to a nearby Chinese restaurant. I was tense and did my best to sound cheerful, but I didn't have much to say. Jeff kept looking at me during dinner and finally asked, "Mom, what's wrong?"

I glared at Rog. "I'm sorry, Jeff. I guess I'm just not myself. I've had this memorial service on my mind and will be happy when it's over so we can get out of here." I paused, then in my most sarcastic tone of voice added, "Only your father likes it here."

Silence followed for a while. Jeff tried again to get through to me. "Is there anything I can do for you?"

"Just being here has helped me. You're my breath of fresh air and ray of sunshine."

"Anything for you, Mom, just name it," he said and squeezed my hand. To ease the tension in the air, Jeff took out his wallet and showed us some recent pictures of Kaitlyn and Tierney. They perked up my spirits. Tierney was a carrot-topped little angel, and Kaitlyn looked adorable in her Mickey Mouse pajamas and pink, fuzzy slippers. I commented how much they looked like Jeff, and the proud dad grinned from ear to ear.

At 6:45 P.M. we reached Carnegie Hall just as people were beginning to arrive. We took our seats in the front row, with Carl and the other guards seated behind us in their TEMAC uniforms. Carl knew everyone and, as the groups arrived, would lean forward and whisper the names of each one: the Rotarians, the fire department, the Alarm Association, the Greenbrier Theater group, and of course, Tod's personal friends. At seven o'clock, the Men of the Greenbrier Barbershop Chorus took their places on the risers, and the service began.

The service was moving and the music inspiring. How pleased Tod would have been when the Rotarians and Men of the Green Brier Barbershop Chorus announced they would be donating a painting to be placed in Carnegie Hall in his memory. After the benediction was given, Tom announced the chorus would close the service with Tod's favorite barbershop song, "The Battle Hymn of The Republic." Then pointing to the empty space in the front row, he said, "This was Tod's place in the chorus. Although he's not with us tonight, I know he's here in spirit." I wept into my handkerchief and was glad that Rose had decided not to attend.

The next day, I began the task I'd put off far too long: packing up Tod's clothes. As I folded them, I held them to my chest, feeling the closeness of him, breathing in the slightly salty scent of his skin that clung to the fabric. How I longed to hear his laughter. When I packed the last shirt and stood looking at the empty closet, I sighed deeply. At that moment, I knew for certain that my son was gone.

We drove home that night and arrived in the wee hours. I was so overwhelmed with sorrow and loneliness that I couldn't sleep. A little after sunrise I took my Bible and went downstairs to the living room. I had to find something that would give me a sign, something to assure me that Tod was with God and at peace. It was then I happened to come across Luke 11:9, "Ask and it will be given; Search and you will find: Knock and the door will be opened for you." I felt as if a dark curtain had been lifted from my mind. I knew that I had to search for the answers to my questions, but I was convinced that God would guide me. This was the beginning of my quest to truly understand Tod's murder. I knew, in time, my prayers would be answered.

# CHAPTER ELEVEN

Because I didn't have a brother, my brother-in-law Bob became very special to me. Well aware of how Tod's death was affecting us, he did some research and found an organization with the frank, frightening name of "Parents of Murdered Children." Bob sent me a package of information about the group, with a letter suggesting we read through it. The organization had chapters throughout the United States with headquarters in Ohio. I called them immediately, only to be told they had no organized support group in our area. They gave me the names of several members who lived elsewhere in New Jersey, and I didn't hesitate to call them, as I desperately needed to talk with someone who knew the trauma I was going through. The people I spoke with were friendly and talked about their tragic stories. They were sympathetic to my suffering, and we cried together over our lost children.

A woman named Sarah not only had lost her son but also her husband, who had a fatal heart attack brought on by their son's murder. "Jan, you are not alone," Sarah said. "Go to any group session and talk with any mother whose child has been murdered. You'll find we're all praying for the same thing, a sign from God, wanting to know our children are with him, wanting to know our loved ones are at peace."

Sally, whose daughter had been murdered, mentioned a support group in Hackettstown, New Jersey, called "Voices for Victims." Hackettstown wasn't far from me, so Sally gave me the phone number. When I called, I don't know why, but I expected a woman to pick up. Instead a man answered, introducing himself as Dick and saying he was the founder of the organization. At first, I felt a little nervous and awkward explaining my reason for calling, but Dick began talking and, within minutes, I felt perfectly at ease. He told me the story of his daughter's brutal murder in New York City. He was still infuriated over how her trial was handled, as well as how badly he and his wife had been treated. It was during her trial that he had realized how much the victims "get kicked around." Dick felt that the system needed to be changed, and he had decided to devote his time to fight for victim's rights. He knew and understood just what I was going through. If only Rog had half of his understanding and sympathy, I thought.

"Jan, if there is anything I can do for you and Rog, please call me," Dick said sincerely. "You must be prepared that the defense lawyer will try to bar you from the courtroom. Defense lawyers don't want the jury looking at distraught parents. And remember this, it won't be your son's murderers who are on trial. It will be your son." I didn't quite understand what he meant by that, but I never forgot his words. Dick sent me a magnet that I kept on my refrigerator and read every day. It bore the words: *"There is no timetable for recovery from the trauma and grief of violent crime."* It gave me great comfort to realize that I had control over my own healing process, no matter what anyone else said.

Rog began making frequent trips to Lewisburg, and from time to time I went along, only to find it extremely depressing. I was becoming more and more resentful of the business and wanted it out of our life. Jeff began urging Rog to sell TEMAC, trying to make him realize that it was impossible to live in one state and run a business in another, but Rog ignored him. Every time I talked about selling TEMAC, it caused a major argument. When he called from Lewisburg one evening, telling me that he had run into an alarm problem and couldn't get home as planned, I accused him of using that as an excuse for not returning to me. Feeling resentful, I suggested that he move to Lewisburg. He evaded the suggestion and soon closed the conversation.

As our household was being turned upside down, my phone calls to Sharon became more and more frequent. One afternoon, when Rog was out on an errand, Sharon asked me a pointed question. "Do you think that running Tod's business may make Rog feel closer to him? Maybe give him some sense of connection with Tod?"

I told her I didn't know, I just felt that the business was destroying our marriage, and I wasn't sure I wanted to be married to him any longer. "If it weren't for Elizabeth and Heather, I would pack up and leave."

"You don't mean that," Sharon said. "If you don't mind me saying so, I think you both need some counseling. Give it some thought."

Our conversation ended, and the more I thought about Lewisburg and the business, the more upset I became. Sharon was right. Something had to be done, and I decided to approach the subject when Rog returned.

Walking into the living room, I sat down on the sofa, still angry. I began releasing my frustration by punching the sofa pillows with my fists and yelling. "Lord, please help me! I don't know what to do or where to turn. I need to know Tod is in your loving care. I can't handle this by myself. If you're listening, Lord, please let me know that you hear me. Lord, help me!"

In the next few moments, I had the experience of my life. My tears suddenly stopped. A calm, peaceful feeling came over me. No one was in the room, yet I felt someone's presence, a slight stirring of air. I sat perfectly still. I didn't know what was happening to me, but suddenly I felt a soft touch on my shoulders, as if someone had come up behind me and placed his gentle hands on me. Of course no one was there. But I knew at that very moment, God was with me, letting me know that Tod was with him. It was the most uplifting experience I have ever had in my life. I believe in miracles, and knew I had just experienced one. My anger disappeared, and for the first time in weeks I felt inner peace. I couldn't believe this had actually happened to me. I sat immobile, trying to recapture the experience and fully understand it.

I was sitting in a daze when Rog walked in. Taking a look at my face, he asked, "Are you okay?"

He listened as I explained, and even then, I'm not sure he really believed me. "I know it sounds unbelievable, but it really happened, just the way I told you," I said. He continued staring at me. As I looked at him, something inside me said that this was the time to confront him.

"Rog, please, sit down, we need to talk." He sat down beside me, and the words started pouring from me like a river. I slowly began explaining how I felt we were drifting in opposite directions, and I wasn't sure where we were headed. I didn't know exactly what he wanted or, for that matter, what I wanted. Tod's death had changed us. I think I shocked him when I said that he wasn't the caring person he used to be, that he was even neglecting his granddaughters. "I feel we're on a sinking ship, and unless we do something, we're going to drown. I don't know if you're willing to salvage what's left of this marriage, but we need to go for help. I can't continue like this, and I don't know what else to do."

He sat with his head down staring at the floor the entire time I was talking. I wasn't sure how he was going to react, or even what he might be thinking. After a few minutes of silence, he looked up at me. "I know you're extremely depressed, and to be perfectly honest with you, I don't know how to cope with it," he replied. He said that my depression was dragging him down and he had made up his mind he wasn't going to let that happen. Also, he said that I needed to come to terms with Tod's death on my own, that no one could help me but me. He did, however, agree to go for therapy and spend more time with the girls.

He started to stand up, and I said, "I'm not through. There's something else I've been giving much thought to." He sank back down on the sofa. I explained that, besides wanting TEMAC removed from our lives, I had a great need to move back home, where I could be near family. I knew Jeff and Trish had busy lives, but we would be able to see them more often, as well as Kaitlyn and Tierney. I felt it would also be nice being close to our parents, who weren't getting any younger.

"What about Rose and the girls?" he asked.

"It would mean that Rose would have to find another job. That's a decision Rose will have to make."

He sat quietly thinking for a few minutes, glaring at the floor. Finally he said, "If that's what you want to do, let's do it."

"What about the business?" I asked.

"I'll sell it when I'm offered the price that Tod wanted for it," he said.

I sighed in exasperation. We were right back where we started. I tried to explain that the business was becoming his top priority, not me or Rose or the girls. It was tearing us all apart. He said that I was being unreasonable, that he was insisting on getting the full value of the business so that there would be more money for the girls' college education.

"That's just an excuse," I replied, hearing anger in my voice. "You know you're not going to get the price you want, which means that you have to hold onto the business. When are you going to admit the truth?" Rog snorted in disgust, and I continued. "Since you can't cope with my depression and I can't cope with your attitude, let's hope a counselor will be able to help us pull it together for us."

"I really hope so," he said turning and walking back to the computer room. I didn't know whether to believe him or not.

I sat back down on the sofa, thinking of my earlier experience and feeling of deep peace. It still boggled my mind, but I knew that I had truly felt the presence of God. I also knew that he answered prayers in mysterious ways. Just then I heard a loud thump at the window and rushed over to look out. A wren lay on the ground, motionless, its wings folded awkwardly under its body. *Poor thing*, I thought. It must have flown into the window and broken its neck. Suddenly, as I watched dumbstruck, the bird's eyes flashed open. It jumped to its feet, gave itself a good shake and flew off like a rocket. As I watched it go, I remembered the baby wren that Tod had tried to save long ago. Could this be another sign? That out of death came life, eternal life? My own little wren had fallen, but God had not forgotten him, either.

That evening, Rose and I sat discussing my idea to sell the house and move. It took her totally by surprise. I suggested she think it over, perhaps even talk it over with the girls. There was no rush; we would wait until the school year ended. "I see nothing to keep us here," she said after thinking it over for a few minutes. "Perhaps a change would be good for all of us. A fresh start, some new surroundings." I was delighted that she felt that way.

Rog began cutting down on his trips to Lewisburg but still spent just as many hours at the computer. He made Elizabeth and Heather happy little girls by reading to them at bedtime again, as he used to. I found a therapist and made an appointment for us. When the big day arrived, I prepared myself by stuffing my handbag with tissues before I left the house.

Mary McQueen was located in a large office building not far from our home. She greeted us with a warm smile. Her office was designed like a living room, with a damask sofa and several comfortable chairs. Rog chose the reclining chair, and I sat down on the love seat. It all seemed so cozy. Mary began asking questions to get a little background before addressing the problems at hand, but when she reached for a notepad and pen, my warm-fuzzy feelings vanished. Rog and I took turns explaining Tod's murder. Then came the point of contention, the TEMAC business. Rog insisted that he should run TEMAC until he found a buyer willing to pay the price. Under Mary's gentle questioning, he admitted that handling the business made him feel closer to Tod, as if he were getting to know him all over again. We discussed my state of depression, how Rog and I had no communication, and Rog's refusal to discuss Tod's death.

"My first obligation is to keep the TEMAC business in operation," he said.

Mary looked at him sternly. He recoiled in shocked when she said, "You need to get rid of that business at any cost. The two of you must get your lives back on track, and that should be your first obligation. Set a goal for when that business will be sold and shoot for it."

Rog gave no reply, although I could tell from his dark expression that he wasn't buying into Mary's demand. When the session was over, we agreed to meet again, after the holidays.

With Thanksgiving approaching, I remembered Tammy and her conversation about wanting us to go to Lewisburg. How I would miss making my usual morning holiday phone call to Tod wishing him a happy Thanksgiving before he went off hunting. On Thanksgiving Day the family gathered at Mom and Dad McQuaid's, and my mother joined us. During the festive Thanksgiving dinner, complete with candied apples and corn bread, Rog announced our moving plans. They were delighted with the idea of having all of us close by, and the move gave all of us something to look forward to.

We returned to New Jersey that Sunday, and out of habit I headed straight for the answering machine the moment I entered the house. As I stood listening to the many messages, I suddenly heard a familiar voice that filled my mind with disgust. "Hi, Mrs. McQuaid, this is Tammy. I wanted to let you to know that I have a few of Tod's things you might like to have returned to you."

I began shouting, and Rog and Rose came running. They listened to the message again. Tammy had left a phone number, and when Rog returned the call, he found it was her sister's number. He asked what items Tammy wanted to return, a request that caught Tammy's sister completely off guard. She had no idea what Rog was talking about, but she did have a surprise for us. "Tammy wants you to return the items you stole from Dad's house," she said. According to Tammy, Tod had given her all his possessions.

Rog made it very clear that nothing was being returned, and neither she nor Tammy were to call our home again. Midmorning of the next day, the phone rang. The caller claimed to be a lawyer friend of Tammy Wilson's, inquiring on her behalf about the "stolen" items. Rog repeated what he told Tammy's sister, adding, "If you or any other friend or family member of Tammy Wilson calls here again, I will take action. Do I make myself perfectly clear?" We found out later that these harassing phone calls were just another one of Tammy's sick games.

A week later Rog and I made a trip to Lewisburg. I'm not sure why I went along, except to try and spend some time together. It was early evening, and I was busy cleaning when there was a knock on the kitchen door. It was Keith, one of the TEMAC guards. He had seen lights and our car in the driveway as he was passing by. We talked for a while, and when the phone rang, I asked Keith to answer it while I washed my hands. As I approached the office, he rolled his eyes and handed me a piece of paper on which he had written one word: Tammy.

I called to Rog, and he immediately got on the extension phone. Tammy began asking Keith questions concerning the business. She wanted to know about Tod's memorial service and why we had him cremated. "I don't know," he answered. "I don't have time to talk." Then he hung up on her. When I asked him how she could know he was in the office, he shrugged and said that maybe she had seen his car from her cell window.

The thought that this sick woman was able to monitor the office disturbed me. Tammy made several more calls over the next few days when we were at the TEMAC office, always when Keith was in. I made an attempt to file a complaint with the state police, asking to have the calls stopped, but Sergeant Sloan explained that as long as she wasn't threatening my life nothing could be done.

Not about to give in without a fight, I called Rick Lorensen. "Mrs. McQuaid, consider the problem taken care of," he said. Later, Judge Jolliffe made it known that, should the calls continue at the TEMAC office or our home, Tammy would permanently lose all phone privileges. The calls ended. I felt glad to know that someone cared about the families of murder victims.

The Christmas season was approaching like a galloping reindeer. Without a doubt, this holiday was going to be hard for me without Tod. It was his favorite time of year, when the little boy in him came out. He loved buying and giving gifts, and I can still hear him telling the girls, "The sooner you go to sleep the sooner, Santa will visit." I'm not sure who was more excited, the girls or Tod. Our Christmas that first year without him seemed solemn and restrained; the holiday just didn't seem right without Tod there cracking jokes and bursting into song every few minutes.

The New Year began, and Rog and I continued weekly therapy sessions, still arguing about the need to sell TEMAC. Nevertheless, I was determined to sell it and began doing research on how to sell a company. I realized that, if the guard business was sold first, we wouldn't need to rent the building. Mr. Elwood and his son, both TEMAC guards, were greatly interested in buying the guard business, but Rog refused to sell at the price they offered. Just in case, I and kept the Elwoods' phone number tucked away in my address book. In the meantime, I placed "for sale" ads in West Virginia papers, hoping to find a buyer. I was also making plans to put our house on the market in the spring, so we could be settled before school started in the fall.

March arrived, along with a special delivery letter from the state of West Virginia. The letter informed us that, on April 24,1991, a hearing would be held in the Circuit Court of Greenbrier County, West Virginia, Plaintiff, versus Harry Joe Johnson, Defendant. I wanted to shove the letter under the carpet. I knew what the outcome was going to be, which angered me greatly. Like it or not, Harry Joe Johnson would be out of prison within five to nine years, thanks to Rick Lorensen's shenanigans and a West Virginia law that allowed for an early release.

# CHAPTER TWELVE

Waiting for Harry Joe Johnson's upcoming trial was hard on our nerves. Just the fact that we would be facing him for the first time made me shudder whenever I thought about it. Not knowing what he looked like, I could only use my imagination. One of the guards described him as resembling Tod. We were told Harry Joe had worn Tod's clothing and hats for a week as he drove around in one of the Broncos, impersonating Tod. Therefore, I expected him to be 5'11," slender, with broad shoulders, dark brown hair, and a mustache.

April 24th, arrived and I was feeling like a lion in a cage. I paced up and down the office unable to concentrate on anything. At 9:30 A.M. Lottie and Carl arrived. Rog and Lottie were going to spend the morning working on the accounting books, although I didn't know how Rog could concentrate. I certainly couldn't. Carl began making out the guard schedules while I paced from one room to another. By 11:00, Carl and Lottie had gone and Rog was ready for lunch. I couldn't even think about food, but Rog insisted we go to the Fort Savannah and grab a bite to eat. I had a lot of nervous energy and expended some of it by glancing at my watch every few minutes.

At 12:30 we headed for the courthouse. As we entered the front door, I was overwhelmed to see at least twenty-five people milling in the lobby. I couldn't imagine what they would be doing there. By the way they were dressed, in flannel shirts, jeans, and crop hats, it was obvious that they weren't court employees. Since there was no directory in the lobby to let us know where the rooms were located, we asked directions from a receptionist, who sent us to the second floor.

We found the courtroom and I was surprised when I pulled on the door to find it unlocked. I peeked in and saw a few people sitting in the back of the room. Rog and I walked in, exchanging smiles with those in the back, not having the vaguest idea who they were. Walking to the front, we noticed a young, blonde woman sitting alone in the front bench on the left-hand side. I approached the front row on the right. "Don't you want to sit over there?" Rog asked, motioning to where the woman sat alone.

"No, let's sit here." I wasn't in the mood for idle chitchat. Glancing over at the young woman, who sat with her head down, looking very sad, I kept thinking she looked familiar, but I couldn't remember where I had seen her.

The people in the back were whispering softly so they couldn't be heard, and I felt as if we were sitting in a doctor's office. When I started to fidget, Rog reached out and took hold of my hand. "You're not nervous, are you?" he asked.

"Why would you think that?" I said. "Now, if only I could keep my knees from shaking."

"You're going to be fine," he said with a laugh.

We were joined by a woman who had been sitting in the back. She slid into the bench behind us, positioning herself between Rog and me. "Are you Tod McQuaid's parents?"

"Yes, we are," I responded

She introduced herself as Connie, a reporter for one of the local papers, and expressed her sorrow about Tod's death. Thinking that she might know the identity of the blonde woman, I asked her who she was. Connie leaned close and whispered, "That's Rachel Johnson."

"Of course!" I said. I'd seen her only once, but I'd remembered her tortured face.

The bailiff entered and took his seat by the side door. I glanced at my watch. 12:45 P.M.

"It was nice meeting you folks," Connie said. "Perhaps we can talk again later." She got up and made her way to the back of the room.

The side door opened again and Harry Joe Johnson entered, his legs in shackles, his lawyer walking beside him. Harry Joe shambled over to Rachel and said a few words to her before sitting down at the defense table.

I was shocked at his appearance: One thing for sure, he didn't resemble Tod: Harry Joe was a slight man about 5'3" with sandy brown hair and mustache. He bore a much stronger resemblance to Yosemite Sam than he did to Tod.

When Rick Lorensen arrived, he walked over to us to say hello and shake hands before proceeding to the prosecutor's table. I glanced around and noticed that Sergeants Johnson and Sloan had come in, taking seats in the back of the room. At 1:00 sharp, the bailiff asked everyone to rise as Judge Jolliffe entered the courtroom and took his seat at the bench. Judge Jolliffe was a dignified looking man with shiny, jet-black hair and dark eyes. As he began speaking, his voice was stern, and from the expression on his face, he looked liked he ruled with an iron fist. That's probably why he had the reputation of being a "hanging judge."

Harry Joe Johnson was called to the witness stand. Judge Jolliffe addressed the fact that his notes indicated there was to be some type of change to a plea pursuant to a plea agreement and asked if that was still the case. Mr. Ford, Harry Joe's attorney, confirmed that it was. Addressing Mr. Lorensen, Judge Jolliffe asked, "Has there been any plea bargaining in this proceeding?"

"Your Honor," Rick said, "the defendant is charged with the felony offense of first-degree murder, along with co-defendants. The State has agreed to accept a plea of second-degree murder in exchange for that plea and truthfully given testimony concerning the facts and circumstances surrounding the death of Tod McQuaid at the trials of Tammy S. Wilson and Roger E. Cline."

Judge Jolliffe glanced at Rog and me, as if to see what our reaction might be. I frowned, and wanted to stand up and shout, "What a cop out! He's agreeing to this plea just to shorten his term. He's as guilty as if he pulled the trigger. I disagree with this whole idea." But I remained silent. Rog must have felt the tension in my body as he reached over and held my hand.

Judge Jolliffe addressed Harry Joe Johnson. "Mr. Johnson, second degree murder carries with it a possible maximum penalty of not less than five nor more than eighteen years in the penitentiary.

Do you have any questions about the charge?"

"No, I don't, sir."

I began shaking my head as Judge Jolliffe glanced our way. Five to eighteen years for taking part in a premeditated murder was ridiculous. In actuality, he would receive only nine years at the most. I couldn't help but wonder had the murder victim been one of Judge Jolliffe's children, would he have been content with that puny sentence?

Judge Jolliffe explained that before he could permit Harry Joe to enter a plea of guilty, he would once again have to explain his constitutional and statutory rights, even though Mr. Ford had already done so. He wanted to make sure Harry Joe knew his rights and what he would be waiving by pleading guilty. "Mr. Johnson," the judge continued, "when you enter a plea of guilty, it's more than just an admission of conduct. If I accept your plea, you will stand convicted, and the only thing left in your case would be for me to decide what sentence should be imposed. Do you understand that?"

"Yes, sir," Harry Joe said.

Then Rick Lorensen addressed the court and asked to summarize the statement that Harry Joe had given on October 24th to officers Johnson and Sloan. The judge agreed, and Rick proceeded with the summary.

"On the 4th day of October 1990, Roger Cline spoke with Harry Joe Johnson and asked him to be an accomplice to a crime. He was told Tammy Wilson wanted to 'knock off' Tod McQuaid. Mr. Johnson thought the idea was crazy and thought they were joking. When he asked Tammy Wilson about what Roger had said, she laughed it off. After that he'd gone home. Tammy Wilson called and asked if he could take part in the perfect crime, would he do it? Mr. Johnson asked what was in it for him; she indicated she would talk about it with him the day of the 5th. On the 5th he came into work and was told to go to a pay phone and talk with Tammy. She told him not to come into work that day, but to park his car at a certain location. She came later and picked him up, and from there went to a lawyer's office.

"Later they went to Tammy Wilson's house on Coffman Hill Road, and Tammy discussed what was going to happen Friday evening. Tammy Wilson told Harry Joe that the plan was for her to take Tod McQuaid out and get him drunk and doped up and take him back to the Coffman Hill house where Harry Joe and Roger Cline were supposed to call her. Later in the evening, Roger Cline and Harry Joe picked up some weapons from the TEMAC office and one of the TEMAC vehicles. They called Tammy at 1:20 A.M. on Sunday, October 6, 1990. She said that the victim wasn't unconscious yet and they should call back in fifteen minutes. They called back later, and she indicated that he was out, so they should get there as fast as they could."

I held a hanky tightly in my hands and chewed on it from time to time to keep my emotions under control. Nevertheless, tears began to stream down my face. Rog put his arm around me and pulled me to his side.

Rick continued: "They parked the car down the road and walked into the house where they were met by Tammy Wilson. She held a 40-caliber pistol belonging to Tod McQuaid. She handed it to Roger who walked into the room and fired three shots, all of which missed Tod McQuaid. Harry Joe went in and indicated to Roger that he had missed. Then Roger went back in and shot again with a 45-caliber pistol, and this time the bullet struck Tod McQuaid in the back of the head. Harry Joe Johnson indicates that he removed carpet from the room in question, took it out along with some towels and burned it. He helped Roger Cline wrap Tod McQuaid in plastic bags and a tarpaulin and placed the body in the back of a blue Bronco belonging to TEMAC. A rug was also placed on the body. Tammy and Harry Joe remained behind and cleaned the house. Bullets that were spent and did not strike the body were collected, along with the empty shell casings. Harry Joe threw the bullets into the woods and then went out and purchased new carpet to replace the area where there was blood. The defendant indicates that he was a willing accomplice who agreed to help for money and position in the company."

Rog bent over, cupping his head in his hands. I could see him taking deep breaths. He was fighting hard to hold back his grief and rage. I continued biting the hanky I held tightly in my hand, but I couldn't stop the flow of my tears.

"Are you entering this plea of guilty because you are, in fact, guilty of the second-degree murder of Tod McQuaid?" the judge asked Harry Joe.

"Yes, your Honor."

Judge Jolliffe, addressing both lawyers, stated that, in lieu of bond, Harry Joe Johnson would be remanded to the custody of the sheriff. "The court will deal, first of all, with the question of whether the plea should be accepted and whether the plea agreement should be approved," he said. "If so, the court will proceed with sentencing."

Much to my dissatisfaction, the Court accepted Harry Joe Johnson's plea and the agreement was approved. Harry Joe received not less than five years and not more than eighteen years for taking part in my son's brutal, senseless murder.

# CHAPTER THIRTEEN

The day had been depressing. I wanted to go home, and if it hadn't been late in the afternoon, I would have suggested we make that ten-hour drive. Instead we met briefly with Rick, who told us that the change of venue for Tammy Wilson's trial had been granted. It would be held at the Morgantown Courthouse, Morgantown, West Virginia, on the court docket for July 29th. Judge Jolliffe would be the presiding judge. "I'd like to suggest we set up a meeting and discuss the Wilson trial on your next trip," Rick said.

Rog agreed, but I just nodded. I was still furious over Harry Joe's light sentence and was in no mood to talk or make nice.

It was going to be a busy summer in more ways than one. Mom and Dad McQuaid were celebrating their 60th wedding anniversary on July 25th, and the family was planning to get together for the big occasion. I offered to make the arrangements for the anniversary festivities, hoping that my duties would help keep my mind occupied so I wouldn't have to think about the upcoming trial of Tammy Wilson.

In the beginning of July, Rog and I met with Rick to go over my written conversations with Tammy Wilson. I was nervous about taking the stand and asked Rick if I could have a copy of my conversations with me just in case. I knew those conversations by heart, but the list would make a handy security blanket. I also told Rick that I wanted to be in the courtroom after we testified, but he avoided making a direct answer. When I pushed the issue, he said, "Mrs. McQuaid, I can't guarantee anything. It depends on the defense attorney." What he really meant was, "Sorry, but the defense won't permit it."

Rog and I asked Bob and Jan if they would attend with us, and they agreed. We reasoned that, even if we couldn't be in the courtroom, our family could take notes, keeping us abreast on the events of the day. I remembered Dick's comment: "The defense will do everything in their power to keep you out of the courtroom."

I had seen Steve Hunter, the defense attorney, in passing at the courthouse. He was a short, stocky man with salt and pepper hair. Each time I had seen him, he was wearing the same green plaid sports coat and tan trousers. On occasion we made eye contact, but he never spoke or smiled. I couldn't imagine what difference it would make keeping us out of the courtroom. As far as I was concerned, Tammy was guilty, and Hunter was going to lose.

Rog and I made many trips to Pittsburgh and finally found a five bedroom house with all the extras that fit our needs. With the family gathering for the anniversary celebration and the Wilson trial at the end of July, our plans were falling into place. Living with twenty adults and eight great-grandchildren in an un-air-conditioned house in hot, humid weather was bedlam but fun. It was one continuous party, with constant feasting, talking and laughter. My heart ached, because Tod was the only one missing. How he would have enjoyed seeing all his cousins one more time!

Sunday afternoon arrived much too soon, which meant Bob, Jan, Rog, and I had to leave for Morgantown. Having the family together had done wonders to help ease my sorrow. We said our good-byes right after lunch, knowing the California gang would be gone when we returned. Long good-byes are a Pittsburgh tradition, but eventually we rolled down the driveway and took off. It was early evening when we arrived in Morgantown. Once we found our motel and settled in, we went out to find a restaurant for a quiet dinner. We sat joking about how peaceful and quiet it was, after the last few days of noisy meals with all the grandchildren.

Back at the motel, we spent the rest of the evening talking about Tod's murder. When the others were ready to turn in for the night, I was still wide awake, tighter than a rubber band stretched to its limit. I tried reading, then finally turned out the light and lay motionless in the dark with thoughts about the trial whirling around in my head. The sound of Rog's voice gently calling my name made me sit up so suddenly I felt as if I had been hit by lightning. I had been dreaming, and my heart was hammering. "It's okay. You were having a nightmare, calling out for Tod." Rog put his arms around me to comfort me as I slowly drifted back to sleep.

Because we didn't know the location of the courthouse in Morgantown, we wanted to get an early start. Bob was up and ready to go by 7:30 A.M., trying to get the rest of us to hustle. We arrived at the courthouse at 8:30 A.M. as planned. Entering the parking lot, I was amazed at the size of this huge, brick structure. We entered on the lower level that I assumed was the basement. People were bustling around, carrying coffee cups, heading in all directions. We wandered around looking for signs that would lead us in the right direction. Finally we asked a security guard, who directed us to take the elevators to the second level, where we found the assigned courtroom. The door was unlocked and the room was dimly lit. Court was scheduled for 9:00; we sat down and waited.

At 8:45 the lights were turned up. Rick Lornesen and Steve Hunter, the defense attorney, arrived, taking their respective places. Rick looked around the room and when he saw us, he came over to greet us. He reminded us that, after the jury selection, Rog and I would be asked to leave the courtroom. He couldn't guarantee we would be able to enter the courtroom after we testified. I had the feeling that he and Steve Hunter had already discussed the subject and Rick couldn't bring himself to tell us that Steve Hunter had refused.

Promptly at 9:00 Judge Jolliffe entered, called court into session, and asked the bailiff to escort Tammy Wilson to the defense table. As she entered the courtroom, Tammy shot us a glance, then quickly looked away. Her hair was pulled back in a ponytail and she wore very little makeup. Her gray flowered dress with a white lace collar made her look like a young schoolgirl. I could feel my body tensing as anger built within me. She had played a game with me, keeping my hopes for Tod alive, all the while knowing the awful truth. What twisted pleasure anyone could derive from such a deception was beyond me.

The twenty prospective jurors were escorted into the courtroom and quickly took their seats. Then twelve jurors were selected, plus four alternates, and all were duly sworn in. It was then that Judge Jolliffe asked, "Does anyone request that the witnesses be separated or sequestered from the courtroom?"

Without hesitation Steve Hunter stood up and replied, "Yes, your honor."

Judge Jolliffe granted his request, glancing our way. I'm sure he knew how I felt by the disappointment in my face. A five minute recess was called, during which Rog and I left the courtroom. From that time forward, we would depend on the memory and notes of Bob and Jan to get a feeling of the trial.

Rog and I walked around the courthouse corridors, checking out the territory, and found the library. Rog became engrossed in a law book. Leaving him there, I continued exploring and found a small room with a few tables scattered with magazines, but soon found it too hard to concentrate on anything. Continuing to explore the halls, I came upon a huge picture window with a ledge large enough to sit on and look out at a courtyard filled with beautiful flowers. As I sat down and enjoyed the flowers glistening in the sunshine, I played all my phone conversations with Tammy over and over in my mind. Without realizing how quickly the morning had passed, I was shaken from my reverie by Rog calling my name as he walked toward me with Bob and Jan. Court had recessed for lunch.

We went outside in the sunshine and walked through the path lined with the roses and lilies I had seen from the window ledge. Their fragrance was delightful. We were able to find a table in a nearby restaurant where we had some privacy to discuss the morning session. Bob handed me his first notebook that was filled with his observations. I was glad when the hour had passed so I could get back to the courthouse and begin reading. Finding the window ledge available, I curled up with Bob's notes and plunged into them.

In his opening statement, Prosecutor Lorensen pointed out that Steve Hunter would be giving Tammy Wilson's version of the evidence as seen through her eyes, and the jury should judge them in terms of how honest and fair they seemed to be and how clearly they presented the evidence. One person pulled the trigger and killed

Tod. He was killed by a bullet to the back of the head. Tammy Wilson did not pull the trigger, but she was the principal in the plan. She encouraged the crime, facilitated the crime, aided and abetted the crime, and was therefore as guilty as the person who did pull the trigger. All three persons intended to be aiding and abetting each other in the killing of Tod McQuaid.

That's interesting, I thought. All three intended to be aiding and abetting each other in killing Tod, but Harry Joe got the plea bargain. I continued reading.

"The evidence will show that, starting on the night on October 5th, 1990, and continuing into the early morning of October 6th, the plot was put into effect. Harry Joe Johnson will indicate that for a period from October 6th to October 15th when the police were first notified, all three remained silent. Tod McQuaid was reported missing on October 15th, 1990. In a statement taken on October 16th, 1990, Tammy Wilson had indicated she had spoken to Tod McQuaid on the 15th and had actually seen him on October 10th.

"The chief medical examiner will testify concerning his identification of the body of Tod McQuaid. He will show the angle of the bullet, which was shot into the head, and that the bullet was shot down in the back of the neck and proceeded into the skull, and was lodged just behind the right eyeball."

I became sick to my stomach. Quickly I raced to the ladies room and vomited into a toilet, crying as I did so. It was a nightmare just to think about my poor son lying helpless. Rog came looking for me and found me crumpled up in a ball on a bench near the ladies room. Taking one look at me, he began asking questions. I just shook my head. "Don't you think you've had enough reading for one day?" he asked. I told him that I was okay. Rog began walking toward the library. I opened the notebook and began reading.

Rick Lorensen asked the jurors to consider four possible verdicts for Tammy Wilson: murder in the first degree, murder in the first degree with mercy, second degree murder, and voluntary manslaughter. "I trust you will return a true verdict in this case, based upon all of the evidence, and that, the truth prevailing, Tammy Wilson will be found guilty."

As I turned the page, I read that defense lawyer Steve Hunter was next to give his opening statement to the jury. He spent a lot of time apologizing for not being used to his new glasses, which didn't make sense to me. Then he went on to say that he and Mr. Lorensen were not on trial and that the jurors shouldn't look at them and say, "The State lawyer did the best job, so we ought to find her guilty," or "The defense did the best job, so we ought to find her not guilty." The attorneys had a job to do and would do it, and not be judged like horses run into a ring. Hunter talked about Harry Joe Johnson being called as a witness, and how he had cut a deal, and that Harry Joe Johnson's testimony should be taken with great caution. The jury should also know that what Rick Lorensen had said and what he was saying were not evidence and should not be considered as evidence. He wanted the jury to focus their attention on the witness chair. He said that the jurors were very important in Tammy Wilson's life, that she was placing her confidence in them and hoped they would weigh the evidence carefully and presume her innocent.

I wanted to be in the courtroom for that, and hear what she would say about Tod. Suddenly a light bulb went on in my brain. *"It's your son that will be on trial."* Now I knew what Dick had meant. Tammy was a gold-medal liar. What sort of lies might she tell about Tod? What sort of lies had she told Mr. Hunter? Did he really believe she was innocent of this "perfect crime" that she had planned and carried out? If he believed her, he was incredibly gullible.

I had finished reading the notebook, and as much as I hated leaving my sunny spot on the ledge, I walked to the library to find Rog with his face buried in a thick book about legal procedure. He really seemed to be getting into it, I thought with a smile. "Are you thinking of taking on a new career?" I asked, walking up to the back table where he was sitting.

He raised his head, confused just for an instant. "No, but it is interesting reading."

I lay Bob's notes on the table in front of Rog. "Tammy Wilson will be taking the stand at some point in time. I'd sure like to be sitting in the courtroom for that, wouldn't you?"

Rog nodded fiercely. "Yes, and I'm damn well going to try to get us in there."

At 3:30 P.M. Rog and I walked back to the courtroom area. The doors opened, and Bob and Jan were the first to appear. Court was adjourned for the day.

"Let's get out of here. My bottom is tired," Jan said. "I wish I had a pillow. Those wooden seats are murder." She snapped her mouth shut and gave me a guilty look. "I mean, they're awful."

"It's okay, Jan," Rog said. "Give me five minutes. I'd like to talk with Rick before we leave."

Walking into the courtroom, we found Rick anxiously gathering up his papers. "The day went well," he said, as he slid documents into his briefcase. "I'm planning to call Harry Joe Johnson to the stand in the morning, and his testimony will probably take up most of the morning."

Rog once again reminded Rick that we wanted to be in the courtroom after we testified. "Folks, I can't promise you that will happen, but I'll try my best to have your wishes met." We walked out of the courtroom together, and Rog and I watched as Rick boarded the down elevator and waved at us, disappearing behind the closed doors. I felt as if our hopes were sinking right along with him.

# CHAPTER FOURTEEN

The next morning we went straight to the second floor. People were gathered in the hall outside the courtroom, talking quietly. Rog spotted Sergeant Johnson and Sergeant Sloan, and we walked toward them to say good morning. They informed us that they were on the day's witness list. I left the group and walked over to the courtroom door, opening it a crack so that I could peek in. Rick turned around and I waved to him, and Bob and Jan went inside to sit down.

"Another exciting day of wandering these halls like lost children," I said to Rog. "Are you going back to the library?"

He nodded and began walking off to his scholarly sanctuary. Once again I roamed the halls, feeling very small and out of place amid the huge marble columns and granite walls. I noticed a young woman and man sitting in two of the many chairs neatly lined up against the wall. I thought the young woman resembled Rachel Johnson, but I had never seen the young man before. They seemed to be carrying on a serious conversation, oblivious to everything going on around them. I made my way to the little sitting room with all the magazines, but I didn't feel like reading. My mind kept pestering me about what was happening in the courtroom. The young woman who had been sitting in the hall walked quietly into the reading room. "Hello," I said, looking up at her with a smile.

"Hello," she replied, and sat down in the chair next to mine. "You're Mrs. McQuaid, aren't you?" I nodded. "I'm Rachel Johnson."

*Wow! I was right!* "Of course. How are you, Rachel?" What a dumb question to ask, I thought. She was probably as depressed as I was.

"I'm okay," she answered, her voice soft, melodic, and a little sad. She was a pretty girl, with a peaches and cream complexion that blended with her beautiful, light blonde hair. Her large blue eyes looked dark with sorrow. "Mrs. McQuaid, would you mind if I talked with you for little while?"

"That would be fine," I replied.

"Please believe me, I didn't have anything to do with the death of your son," she murmured. "I didn't know Tod well, but he was a nice person, and I liked him." She couldn't understand why Harry had become involved in such an awful plan. She had stopped at the TEMAC office on the 5th of October to leave a message for Harry, and when she found he wasn't there, she left the message with Tod. She said Tammy had called her and asked her to bring her young son to the office to help her. Rachel had no idea what Tammy meant, but agreed anyway. When she arrived, Tammy said that she wanted Rachel to help by cleaning the office and taking care of Tammy's little boy. She also wanted them to stay at the TEMAC office. When Rachel refused, Tammy became angry and insisted she wouldn't have it any other way. Tammy didn't hesitate to show her that she had a gun and would use it if she had to.

Rachel was soft-spoken and seemed calm, but she kept twisting an embroidered handkerchief that she was holding. She said she asked Harry Joe what was going on, and he told her to do exactly what Tammy said. Tammy had her run some errands, but she had to leave her little boy with Tammy, which distressed her because she was so afraid of the woman. Rachel didn't understand what was going on, but later figured out that Tammy thought that, if she had Harry's family with her, Harry wouldn't talk. "I asked Tammy when Tod was coming back, and Tammy never answered. I'm so angry with Harry Joe! I can't tell you how sorry I am."

I wasn't sure what she wanted from me, other than to believe her innocence. "I'm sorry that you and your son became Tammy's victims, too," I said. "It's too bad Harry Joe chose wrong over right, but now he must pay the consequences. Unfortunately, you and your little boy will have to suffer too."

Rachel looked at me with mournful eyes. "Thank you," she said softly. "I hope I didn't take up too much of your time." She got up and left as quietly as she had come in.

The more things I heard about Tammy Wilson, the more I realized how diabolical she was. I only wished that Tod could have avoided her.

I got up to walk a little bit, and saw Rog heading my way. At that moment the courtroom doors opened, and Bob and Jan appeared. A ten minute recess had been called. Jan had scurried to a pay phone to find out if her grandchild had been born yet. When she returned, just in time to reenter the courtroom, she gave us a quick glance. "No baby yet!"

The walls were starting to get to me, so Rog and I headed for the front door and walked outside into the flower garden. Finding an empty bench we sat down and began people-watching. Among the radiant flowers, I soon found myself relaxing from the stress of being inside the courthouse. I didn't want to leave, but it was getting close to noon. Bob and Jan wouldn't have the vaguest idea where to find us. As we stepped off the elevator, we saw them waiting in the hall.

"Let's get out of here," Jan said, discreetly rubbing her hip. "I need a change of scenery and a soft seat."

"How did it go this morning?" I asked Jan as we grabbed a park bench in the shade, waiting for Rog and Bob to bring back lunch from the local vendor. Jan had wisely bought a newspaper and, covering it with a handkerchief, made herself a comfy cushion.

"Harry Joe is testifying. I can't begin to tell you everything. Bob is writing like crazy. You'll have to read his notes."

The guys finally arrived with sandwiches and drinks. Surprisingly, the park benches began to fill quickly with other people doing the same thing. In a short while it was time for Bob and Jan to return to the courtroom. Rog and I sat outside a little longer, until it became too warm even for me. I followed Rog to the courthouse library. When we entered, I saw two people sitting at a table by the door. After we exchanged glances, they quickly turned their heads away. I kept following Rog as he led the way to the table at the opposite end of the room. "Who are those people?" I whispered.

Rog snorted derisively. "I believe they are Tammy Wilson's

mother and Roger Cline's uncle. They were here this morning," he said, as if he had tasted something rotten.

"Why aren't they in the courtroom?" I asked. "Wouldn't you think Tammy's mother would want to be in the courtroom, giving her daughter support?

"Let's not concern ourselves about those people, all right?" Rog said. Then he smiled. "Why not grab a law book and read that for awhile? A little entertainment is just what you need."

"Thanks but no thanks," I replied, glancing at the other two people. Their presence made me feel uneasy. "I think I'll take a walk." I took off before he could change my mind, but I knew that I wouldn't get too far. I was amazed that the huge courthouse had so few places to escape to, so to speak. Not even a coffee shop. After a hour or so, the courtroom door opened, and Sergeants Johnson and Sloan ambled out. They had finished their appearances on the stand and were on their way back to Lewisburg. I'm sure they were relieved when the case broke and they arrested Tammy. I thought about the great satisfaction I would feel if only I could lock Tammy in a jail cell forever.

After court was adjourned for the day, I met Bob and Jan and asked them to get Rog from the library while I took a few minutes to talk with Rick. I walked into the courtroom where Tammy and Steve Hunter were still conversing, and it unnerved me a little to be so close to her. I sighed in relief when the bailiff approached her and escorted her out of the courtroom. Rog joined me and asked Rick when he thought we would be called to the stand.

"It won't be tomorrow, but I plan to call Mrs. McQuaid the next day and perhaps you the following day," Rick said. Suddenly his voice became very soft and sympathetic. "Mrs. McQuaid, I have a picture I plan to present to you on the stand. I'm sorry, but it's of Tod, after his decease, and it's not a pleasant sight. Would you have a problem viewing it?"

"I don't know," I replied, my nervous twinges returning. "Perhaps, especially if I could look at it ahead of time."

"When court adjourns tomorrow, I'll show it to you," Rick replied. "But keep in mind, it could be disturbing."

That evening I kept thinking about the picture, wondering how horrible it could possibly be. It was a quiet evening for us in the motel room. Rog and Bob became engrossed in a ballgame on TV, and Jan began working on a cross-stitch picture for the new baby's room. I curled up on the bed and began reading the notebook with Harry Joe Johnson's testimony.

Harry Joe Johnson had said he spent two years, nine months, and two days as a Navy ordinance man for A6 aircraft and was a plane captain before receiving an honorable discharge due to stress. When he was hired at TEMAC, he met Roger Cline, an hourly employee who worked as a maintenance man.

"One day Roger and I were driving around when he told me Tammy Wilson wanted to knock off Tod McQuaid and would I be interested. I called her, and when I asked her, she just laughed it off. But when I got home from work Tammy called around 10:00 P.M. She asked if I could take part in a perfect crime, would I do it? I asked her what was in it for me."

The prosecutor asked, "Was there any response as to what might be in it for you?"

"Yes, an amount of money and an executive position."

"Who made that response to you?"

"Tammy Wilson."

"On what date did this conversation take place?" the prosecutor asked.

"October 4th, 1990. The next day I arrived at work at 8:30 A.M. and Roger Cline stopped me below the TEMAC office and told me not to report for work. Instead I was to go the nearest phone and call Tammy, which I did. She told me to park my car somewhere nearby and she would pick me up, which she did."

Harry Joe went on to say that they drove to see her lawyer and Tod's lawyer, but he didn't know what was discussed since Tammy talked with them alone. Then they went to her house on Coffman Hill and met Roger Cline there around eleven or twelve o'clock.

"What was the date that this meeting took place?"

"October 5th, 1990. Tammy said she wanted to kill Tod McQuaid and take over the company. If we helped out, we would get an executive position in the company and a large amount of money."

Harry Joe said that Tammy wanted to kill Tod because "she wanted the whole company to herself." When pressed, he said that they might have been lovers, but he wasn't sure. When I read this, I could only think that Tod was like any normal young man with physical needs. I had no doubt that he may have slept with Tammy, but I didn't believe for one minute he was interested in marrying her.

Harry Joe said that he wasn't surprised that Tammy wanted to kill Tod. When the judge asked him why, Harry Joe replied that "human life didn't mean nothing to her."

The next section of testimony was very difficult for me to read, as it described just how the murder was planned and committed. Harry Joe said that Tammy was supposed to get Tod "drunk and drugged up" and take him back to Coffman Hill. He and Roger were supposed to call her, see if he was out, then go up to the house. Roger said he would do the shooting. The planning session lasted two or three hours, then they discussed how to dispose of the body. Roger Cline was to take it up to Ohio. "Tammy didn't want the body discovered for a long time, and Roger suggested acid."

"Did anyone of you, meaning yourself, Roger Cline, or Tammy Wilson, ever express reservation about doing this particular deed?" Rick asked.

"No, sir."

"Mr. Johnson, did you have a personal dislike for Tod McQuaid which allowed you to take part in this?"

"No, I did not."

"Then why did you take part in it?"

"For money."

I couldn't understand how Harry Joe Johnson could be so dumb. Tod was building his business and could only afford to pay a minimum wage. If Harry Joe had just waited and done a good job, Tod would have rewarded him generously. If only he'd had the chance!

Harry Joe went on to say that he met Roger at the TEMAC office at midnight. They waited for the blue Bronco, which was out on a run. When it came back, they went into the TEMAC office and got a tarp and two guns, a Smith & Wesson and a Magnum 357. Roger took the blue Bronco, and Harry Joe got in his car, then both drove to the nearest phone. Roger called Tammy, but she said that Tod wasn't out yet. Roger called back in fifteen minutes, around 12:35 or 12:40 A.M. but she said to call back later. At 1:00 Roger called again, and she said to come over. On the way to Tammy's house in the Bronco they ran into Roger Cline's cousins, who were parked near Tammy's driveway. Afraid that the cousins would hear the shots, Roger and Harry Joe bluffed them into believing that cops were coming to arrest somebody and that they should leave immediately. Once the cousins left, the two men parked the Bronco and entered the house, where Tammy was waiting for them.

"What kind of state was she in? Was she dressed?" Rick Lorensen asked.

"Yes, she was dressed. She had a .40 caliber Smith & Wesson in her hand. She said, 'I got this away from Tod. Now do it.' Tod was on the bedroom floor, lying on sheets and blankets."

"How was he clothed?"

"He was, I think, wearing jockey shorts. I ain't sure. Roger went in and fired the .40. Thinking he hit Tod, he walked outside, drove the Bronco up to the house, and took down the tailgate."

"What did you do?"

"I went in and checked the body to make sure Tod was dead, but he wasn't. I went out and told Roger that he missed, and he came in and fired again from about ten or twelve feet. I went in and checked the body again, but he had only hit the floor. Tod didn't move or nothing. I told Roger that he missed again, so he went in and fired again, and he missed that time too. Then Roger got mad and tried to hand me the gun and told me to do it. I told him, 'No, I ain't going to do it.' Then he grabbed the .45 caliber off the kitchen table, went in, and fired ten to twelve feet away again, and that time he hit Tod."

"Where did Roger hit him?"

"The back of the head."

I began crying so hard that I couldn't see to read any more. Rog reached over and gently took the notebook out of my hands. "Why don't you climb into bed and get some sleep? Tomorrow is another day."

"You're right," I said, blowing my nose. "Those three evil savages don't deserve to live, at least in my opinion."

I must have slept soundly, because the smell of coffee woke me up. Rog and Bob had gone out for coffee and bagels. It was almost eight o'clock and I had to hustle. We were back in the court house at 8:45. For Rog and me, it was back to the same boring routine, so I asked Bob for the notebook.

"Jan, do you think it's a good idea to read anymore of this?" Bob asked, draping his arm protectively over my shoulder.

I looked up at him and smiled. *He's the greatest brother-in-law any one could have*, I thought. "I'm okay, honest. Thanks for asking, but don't worry about me."

Bob reluctantly handed me the notebook, then he and Jan proceeded into the courtroom. For a change of pace, I decided to join Rog in the library where there were many windows. I sat at the far end of a table where the sun was streaming in through a window and opened the book to where I had left off. Harry Joe was still answering questions.

Harry Joe said that Tod was lying on his right side. Although he had not actually seen the bullet strike Tod, he checked out the body after the fourth shot and saw blood and gray matter oozing from Tod's head. Tammy was getting scared that someone would hear the shots and come in and investigate. They wrapped the body in trash bags, tape, the tarp and the blankets he was lying on. Then they carried the body to the Bronco, put it inside, and put the rug over the body to hide it from passersby. After Roger left, Tammy and Harry Joe tried to clean up the blood by wiping it up. When that didn't work, they tore up the carpet. Blood had seeped underneath the carpet and was getting on the tile. They used rug cleaners to try to cleanse the area, then took the bloody piece of carpet outside, poured gasoline on it and burned it.

"What happened to the victim's clothes? Where did you put them?"

"I don't know. Tammy did something with them. I left Tammy's around 4:30 in the morning. Before I went home I went back to the TEMAC office and reloaded the weapons."

If Tammy got rid of Tod's clothes, as Harry Joe claimed, why did I find his cowboy boots and sweater side-by-side on the floor? If she had drugged him enough to knock him out, he wouldn't have been able to remove his clothing before he lay down on the floor. I had watched him remove his cowboy boots on several occasions, and they were not easy to take off. I passed my thought on to Rog.

"Jan, there are going to be many questions we will never have the answers to. Dwelling on them will drive you crazy, so let it go," he said.

I returned to the notebook.

"Mr. Johnson, what was the schedule like after this incident in terms of running TEMAC Security?"

"Very hectic. We had to cover up for Tod not being there."

"How involved was Tammy, prior to Tod McQuaid's death, in actually running day-to-day operations?"

"She was more like a secretary and took care of paperwork."

"After the death of Tod McQuaid, did her role change?"

Harry Joe explained how Tammy began to take over the paperwork and control the guards and the alarm system. When people, including Carl, asked about Tod, Harry Joe said that he had gone off for the weekend, an excuse that Tammy had suggested.

I found that statement to be interesting. When Tod went off for weekends, it was to come home to visit us and the girls. Carl was no dummy. He knew when Tod was going to be gone because Tod told him, so he could be reached at all times. A liar like Tammy should have been able to devise a better excuse; of course, those that didn't know Tod would believe her.

"Mr. Johnson, when did you first talk to the police about the whereabouts of Tod McQuaid?"

"Around the 16th of October, when they investigated the radio call that Tod McQuaid had been shot."

"Do you know where the radio call originated from?"

"It didn't originate nowhere. It didn't really happen. Tammy Wilson told me to tell the state troopers that there had been a call saying that Tod had been shot. It was supposed to have occurred that night. It was a trick to throw the police off the track."

"When did you become aware that Tod McQuaid's body had been found?"

"On October 21 or 22, when Roger called up Tammy. Then we learned Roger turned himself in and told the police where the body was."

Rick Lorensen then asked to back up a little and questioned Harry Joe about replacing the bloody section of carpet. Harry Joe recalled how he and Tammy had gone to True Value to get a piece of new carpet, and that Tammy had paid for it by check on the TEMAC account. She had signed the check, although she didn't have the authority to do so. In fact, Tod had told Harry Joe that "nobody had authority to sign checks except him." Tammy had forged Tod's signature.

Rick has asked Harry Joe if he remember picking up a prescription for valium for Tammy Wilson from Bill Coleman, and Harry said he did not.

I laid down the notebook for a moment and thought about what I had just read. If Roger Cline agreed to do the shooting, and Tammy had arranged it, why had he refused when Tammy offered him ten thousand dollars to shoot her ex-husband? Why did he pass up that big money and then turn around and agree to shoot Tod? Roger Cline turned himself in and told the police where he took Tod's body, and I had to admit that we were all thankful for that. If it had been up to that bitch, Tod would have never been found. But that didn't change the fact that they were all murderers. I picked up where I had left off.

"Mr. Johnson, what did Tammy say to you about Roger turning himself in?"

"She said it was stupid. We were to make up another story to tell the police, that me and her went up to the Coffman house, found the blood and cleaned it up, thinking it was Tod McQuaid that shot Roger Cline, but then Roger Cline showed up, and he threatened us, so we did not turn him in."

"Where did this conversation take place about this story?"

"It took place at the TEMAC office around three o'clock in the morning, after Roger turned himself in." Harry Joe said that he himself was arrested on October 23rd at the lumber yard in Ronceverte. Trooper Sloan and Trooper Johnson came up to him, and he decided to tell them the truth because Tammy had threatened him. She said she wanted him to leave the state but had to leave his pregnant wife. Tammy promised to send him his wife and baby later, and Harry Joe took that as a threat.

"When was it she said this?" Rick Lorensen asked.

"About two hours before the state police showed up. Tammy told me to 'keep to the story' if the police talked to me. When they arrived at the lumber yard and read me my rights, I told them what happened."

"Were you offered any promise of leniency or any such thing by the police to give a statement?"

"No, I gave them my statement, and they arrested me for murder."

I closed the notebook. I had read enough. This particular selection was a book straight out of hell. Only this was no Stephen King novel that would frighten me for a few minutes or even a night or two, then fade into the background and let me get on with my routine. No, this horror was real, and it would stay with me for the rest of my life.

I couldn't help but wonder what kind of upbringing these three had had. It was hard to imagine Tammy as an innocent little girl, playing with dolls or stuffed animals, like Elizabeth and Heather. There was no doubt in my mind that Tammy was on the wild side for most of her life, willing to do anything to get what she wanted.

The court adjourned for lunch, but time passed quickly, and

soon we had to return to the courthouse. Bob and Jan returned to the courtroom, and Rog and I went back to the library.

Steve Hunter cross-examined Harry Joe, and began by asking him basically the same questions as the prosecutor. I wondered if he did this on purpose, thinking he could catch Harry Joe in a lie.

"Harry, was Tod easy to get along with?"

"Yeah."

"Did the two of you ever have harsh words?"

"No."

"What about Roger? Did Tod ever pick on him? "

"He picked on him a couple of times."

"Did you ever get any money from Tammy Wilson — cash, checks, stock certificates, any deed, bill of sale, or other documents purportedly transferring any interest in the corporation related to TEMAC — for the alleged crime she had plotted with you?"

"No, I did not."

"Harry, were you given a promotion or any advance in pay after Tod McQuaid's death while you were at TEMAC?"

"Yes. I started out at minimum wage at three sixty-five and went up to four dollars."

"Were you present at any time there was conversation between Roger Cline and Tammy Wilson prior to the 4th day of October concerning killing Tod McQuaid?"

"Yes. About the first couple weeks after I started there, Tammy asked me a couple of questions, like what would be an easy way to kill a person, and I told her poisoning. I thought it was stupid, but after this happened I found out why."

"Harry, where was Tammy Wilson standing when Roger Cline shot Tod McQuaid?"

"Between the dining room and the kitchen."

"Did Tammy ever do any crying or screaming?"

"No."

"Can you remember what else happened after the first shot?"

"I went and checked the body, and Tammy stood there in the door and watched me. When I told Roger he missed, he couldn't believe he missed at that close range, so he stood in the same place and fired the second shot and missed again. He couldn't believe he missed again, and fired the third shot and missed again. I called him an idiot."

"Why didn't you shoot Tod?"

"I was the cleanup man. I wasn't supposed to shoot anyone."

"That's why you pled guilty to second degree murder?"

"The way I seen it, I done the same crime they did, except I came out and told the truth."

"For that you got what they say is a sweetheart deal?"

"I think five to eighteen years ain't a sweetheart deal. I'm still young. I can do life, but I have a son I would like to raise."

*How dare he!* I thought. What about Tod's two little girls? He didn't think twice about taking Tod away from his little girls forever. I could only hope Tod's death would haunt him for the rest of his life.

Mr. Lorensen approached Harry Joe for re-examining. "Could you determine why Tod couldn't move when the shots were fired?"

"Tammy said that he was doped up on Valium, mushrooms, and alcohol. After the first shot, I saw his fingers twitch and his chest rise and lower."

"So you could see he was actually breathing?"

"Yes, he was."

"That's all I have, your Honor," Mr. Lorensen replied.

I closed the notebook, deciding it was time to take a walk and clear my head. I strolled up to the courtroom doors, hoping to catch a few words, and found a woman and young girl standing in the hallway. The woman had her arm around the girl. Not knowing who they were, I didn't pay much attention to them. I was concentrating on being able to hear through the thick doors. The woman left the girl and walked toward me. "Aren't you Mrs. McQuaid?" she asked.

"Yes, I am," I replied, wondering how she knew me.

"I'm Mrs. Echols, Roger Cline's mother, and this is his sister. Mrs. McQuaid, I want you to know that Roger didn't kill your son. Tammy did, not my boy. Roger's very concerned about you and Mr. McQuaid," she said, beginning to cry. "You have no idea how my heart is breaking. I don't know how I'll handle going to prison to visit him."

I stared at her aghast. *Where was this woman coming from?* I thought. She had some nerve saying that to me. "Excuse me, but your son pulled the trigger and shot my son in the head. As for his concern about us, it's a little late for that now, isn't it? Your son should have thought about Tod's little girls before pulling the trigger. Mrs. Echols, you may think that your heart is breaking, but in fact, you are really very lucky, because your son is alive and well. When you visit him in prison and tell him how much you love him, think of me. I'll be putting flowers on my son's grave."

Shaking, I turned and strode away from her. I was so upset I threw myself into the nearest corner and stood there weeping. Rog saw me and immediately came over to me. Without asking any questions, he ushered me into the empty magazine room. "That woman had some nerve," I mumbled, and explained my incident with Roger Cline's mother.

"Well now, she's a mother too," Rog said. "It will be hard on her to visit her son in prison."

"Sure, take her side," I growled. "Her son is alive. But not Tod. We'll never see him again, never hold him. And you have the impudence to stand there telling me *I* should feel sorry for *her*?" *How could Rog betray me this way?* I thought.

"Jan, I'm not taking her side," he said firmly. "I'm only saying that she feels awful about the whole situation."

Just then the courtroom doors opened for a fifteen minute recess. Bob and Jan spotted us and came into the magazine room. Seeing me so upset, they began asking me questions, and Rog said that he would explain later. Jan ran off to the pay phone again, and Bob headed for the water fountain with Rog beside him. I sat down and began flipping pages in a magazine, seeing nothing. I sat there for quite a while, alone, trying to calm down. I was furious, and it took me some time to realize that the person I was so furious with was not Mrs. Echols or Rog, but the woman who had killed my son. Finally I walked to the library and began reading the testimony of Sergeant Johnson.

Sergeant Johnson said that on Monday, October 15th, Trooper Bruce Sloan called him and said that had a report of Tod McQuaid having been shot in the Meadow Bridge area of Fayette County. Johnson and Sloan sought out the person that Tod had signed a warrant against, then interviewed several people that evening. The investigation continued for several weeks. On October 17th Sergeant Johnson called Tammy Wilson into his office and obtained a statement from her, a tape-recorded conversation that took about two hours. On October 24th, he took two statements from Tammy, one in the afternoon and one at night.

Steve Hunter asked Trooper Johnson to describe the circumstances of making the second statement, and the officer said that he and Trooper Sloan had arrested Harry Joe Johnson after he implicated Tammy. The two officers went directly to the TEMAC office and placed her under arrest, then drove her to the Lewisburg state police office.

The defense attorney showed Johnson State's Exhibit No. 3, Tammy's second statement, in the officer's handwriting. At that point, Rick Lorensen stood up and asked if Trooper Johnson might be allowed to read the statement. Judge Jolliffe granted his permission, and the sergeant began reading.

"On Friday night October 5th, 1990, Tod McQuaid and I went to the Fort Savannah Inn. We drank some gin and tonics. We stopped in the TEMAC office about twelve or twelve-thirty, and got to Coffman Hill about 1:00 A.M. Tod and I were in the white Bronco. We drank for some time until 2:00 A.M. October 6th, Sunday morning. Tod had taken valium and other pills and drank heavily. He passed out at 2:00 A.M. and went in and lay on the floor of the bedroom. Roger Cline and Harry Johnson came in. They had driven the blue Bronco. They had a couple of guns, Tod's guns. They kept me in the kitchen while Roger went in and shot three, maybe four times. Tod was so drunk he didn't move. Harry and I didn't shoot any guns. Roger and Harry wrapped Tod in a garbage bag, a big thing that looked like a tent, and maybe a blanket, then they carried him out and put him in the blue Bronco. Roger left en route to Ohio. He said he was going to put the body in a cave. Harry took the bullets and shell casings and disposed of them, and I believe Harry burned the carpet and towels outside. Harry put new carpet down, or someone did. We drove back to the TEMAC office about 5:00 or 6:00 A.M., and I stayed there and Harry drove home. The motivation behind Roger shooting Tod was that Tod had touched my six-year-old daughter while she was bathing at the TEMAC office on Sunday of the weekend before October 6th while my daughter was visiting me that weekend. I saw Tod touch her all over. Tod was clothed at the time. My daughter doesn't want to be near me now. I asked Rose McQuaid about this, and she told me it was the reason Tod had no visitation."

This garbage made me so furious that I almost ripped the page in half. Saying Tod wasn't allowed to visit his daughters was just another lie. What she said about Tod and her daughter was a lie, too. And she had never talked with Rose about such a thing. I continued to read her statement, my hands quivering with anger.

"I don't know why Roger would kill Tod McQuaid. Roger said he did it because of what Tod had done to Tod's daughters, and he said he had seen Tod hit me once. I don't know why Harry got involved. I think we are all crazy. How could we do this? I didn't think Roger or I thought we'd go through with it. Harry told Rachel that he and I walked in after the fact. I didn't take any money, and I'm glad it's over. It's a hell of a thing to have to live with. There were just too many people that took things too seriously. I love Tod still; that's why it's hard. The second it happened I was sorry. It's mostly my fault, and I'm punishing them for helping me. I really didn't think Roger would do it. I have sat down at the TEMAC office these last two weeks and run it like Tod would have wanted me to. I'm really glad it's over."

Reading her lies made my blood pressure rise. My son was certainly not a child molester.

Mr. Hunter re-questioned Trooper Sloan, but apparently Bob did not have a chance to write down the first question. He did, however, write down the trooper's answer.

"Mr. Johnson said he had received a call from his employer, Mr. McQuaid, and that Mr. McQuaid told him he had been shot on a mountain somewhere behind Meadow Bridge. I tried to obtain as much information as I could from Mr. Johnson, but he seemed confused and really couldn't provide me with much detail. So I proceeded to the TEMAC office, which is located just down the street from our office in Lewisburg. When I arrived I was met by a gentleman who informed me that he was Mr. Johnson and by Ms. Tammy Wilson, who informed me she was the operations manager for the security company."

"Did she say anything about having received a call from Tod McQuaid?"

"Yes, on this particular night, October 15th, somewhere around 8:00 P.M. They weren't specific about the exact time they received the call. When she recognized his voice, she asked him if he was coming in, and he stated, 'Stop and listen. I have been shot on the mountain behind Meadow Bridge. Call Carl, he'll know what to do.' Miss Wilson asked Mr. McQuaid how badly he was hurt, and he responded, 'Don't worry about that. Call Carl, he'll know what to do.' She said at that point the phone went dead."

"Trooper Sloan, was there anyone else in the TEMAC office at the time these statements were given to you?"

Sergeant Sloan said that Carl arrived shortly after he did and said that he had no idea what was meant by the statement, 'Carl would know what to do.' Sloan then tried to obtain more information from Tammy and Harry Joe, asking them if they knew where Tod had been going. Tammy said that when Tod left on October 10th, he told her that he intended to find Evelyn Gettman, his former girlfriend. He had obtained warrants for her alleging that said she had broken into Tod's office in September and stolen some items. Tammy had said that Tod was disappointed that the sheriff's department had not arrested her on the warrants, and he was going to look for her himself in Meadow Bridge.

Although there was a felony warrant for Evelyn Gettman, Sloan said he didn't know where to look in Meadow Bridge, so he contacted Trooper Johnson, who was assigned to that area. They arrived in Meadow Bridge at 9:45 P.M. and shortly afterwards located Ms. Gettman and arrested her on the warrant. They took her to Summers county, where she was arraigned by the magistrate.

"Trooper Sloan, was Ms. Gettman a suspect for you and Trooper Johnson insofar as the reported shooting of Tod McQuaid or his disappearance was concerned?"

"Yes, based on the information that Miss Wilson had provided me. She felt Ms. Gettman was responsible for Mr. McQuaid's disappearance."

"What did you do then?"

Sergeant Sloan said that they searched Meadow Bridge and talked to several people, but after three hours found no leads as to Tod's whereabouts. On October 23rd, Sloan received a phone call from the Beckly State Police dispatch, saying Tod's body had been found in Belmont county, Ohio.

On October 24th, they spoke with Harry Joe Johnson and discovered discrepancies in his previous statement. He initially said he was present when Tod called in on October 15th, saying he was shot. Sloan learned the date of death was prior to that time. Then Harry Joe told him that Tod was killed at Tammy's house in Ronceverte, and that he, Tammy and Roger were all present.

"After taking the statements, was there further investigation?"

"We contacted the Greenbrier magistrate to obtain search warrants for the residence of Ms. Wilson and searched the property. When we obtained the statement from Harry Joe Johnson, he indicated to us that Ms. Wilson had initially asked him to obtain a drug that would render Mr. McQuaid unconscious."

The prescription for twelve valium tablets was in the name of Tammy Wilson and dated September 2nd, 1990. It was written by Dr. J. Vascik. Sloan stated that valium, also known as Diazepam, could render a person unconscious.

After a few more questions, the prosecutor and the defense were finished examining witnesses, and the jury was dismissed. Court was adjourned until 9:00 A.M.

I stopped and sat quietly, trying to digest all I had read. I felt as if I had aged twenty years. My body ached. I was angry, and my heart was filled with hate and the desire for revenge. I had been told, "The pain will never be over." How could it? I had a void in my life that could never be filled.

Bob and Jan and Rog found me in the magazine room, resting my head on the notebook. Court had adjourned. On the way out

Rog bought a Lewisburg newspaper that was reporting the trial, and we read the article over dinner. The article referred to Tammy's statement alleging that Tod was a pedophile.

When we returned to the motel, I took it upon myself to call Tammy Wilson's ex-husband about this accusation. He wasn't home, so his wife and I discussed the article. She explained that they, too, were extremely upset. She said that she and her husband talked at great length with their daughter. "Our daughter couldn't believe her mother would say such a thing," she said. "She told us that Tammy was lying, that Tod never touched her."

When I called home and told Rose about the article and Tammy's version of her conversation with her, Rose was incensed. "That bitch! I never talked with her, so why would she say something like that? It wasn't true! Tod came home all the time to visit the girls, and you know as well as I do that the court granted him visitation rights to take the girls to West Virginia when Heather turned five. Where is that lunatic coming from?"

That fact that Tammy could tell this terrible lie and get away with it infuriated me. The words, "It will be your son who is on trial," kept haunting me. Even after I finally got to sleep that night, I woke up often, that terrible phrase rattling in my ears.

# CHAPTER FIFTEEN

Court had ended for the day as Rog, Bob, Jan, and I stood waiting for Rick Lorensen to come out of the courtroom. This was the day I was to be shown the picture of Tod in preparation for the stand. The longer we waited, the more nervous I became. I wasn't sure I wanted to go through with this. Rick arrived and apologized for his delay as we walked down the hall to a small room the size of the magazine room. Before entering, he asked Bob and Jan to wait outside. Rog walked in behind me. The room was dark except for the glow of a lamp on a desk near the door.

"Please remember, I told you this was a disturbing sight," Rick said, laying the picture under the desk lamp. We turned around, and I stood in shock as I looked at what Rick Lorensen called a picture of Tod. Rog put his arm around me and squeezed my shoulder. Suddenly I felt sick to my stomach and short of breath. The room suddenly became stifling. How much more did Rick Lorensen think I could possibly take? I had been in a living hell for weeks, and he had the gall to show us this?

The picture showed a skull and some shoulder bones with a silver and gold chain around the neck. My murdered son's naked skull. What did Rick Lorensen expect me to say? I knew it was Tod.

"Mrs. McQuaid, I know this is difficult and shocking. It's okay for you to express your emotions. Why don't you come and sit down?" Rick said. I did as he said, weeping, still gasping for breath. "Tomorrow when you're on the stand, I am going to show you this picture. Do you agree that it's Tod?"

"Of course it is!" I shouted angrily.

"Forgive me," he asked softly, "but how do you know? The defense may ask you."

"Any person in his right mind would know better than to ask that question," I murmured. "I recognize the neck chains, and even though it is only his skull, it still resembles Tod." I doubled over, holding my head in my hands. My tears seeped through my clenched fingers.

"Take your time in answering the questions tomorrow, Mrs. McQuaid," Rick said, "and you'll be fine on the stand."

"She's been through enough," Rog said, and without another word, he bent over, took my hand to help me up from the sofa and guided me toward the door. As far as he was concerned, it was over.

The minute we got outside that door, I broke down in wrenching sobs. *What was Rick trying to do, push me over the edge?* I thought. "I can't do it. I can't take the stand knowing I'll have to look at that picture again," I said. "That picture will live with me until the day I die. That's not the way I want to remember my son."

"I don't know what Rick was trying to do," Rog answered, "but it was definitely not a kind thing to do. Maybe he'll change his mind and decide not to show it to you tomorrow."

Bob and Jan came walking down the hall when they saw us standing outside the door. "Good grief, what happened in there?" Jan asked, her eyes widening in concern. Rog explained to Bob and Jan about the picture of Tod and the shock to my system. I couldn't get that brutal image out of my mind. I didn't want to take the stand, and yet I desperately wanted Tammy Wilson put behind bars forever. Maybe confronting the truth within the picture would help Rick convict Tammy. It was the only shred of hope I could cling to.

That night at the motel, I went to bed early and tried to block out the entire world. After a while, I fell into a fitful sleep and soon awoke with a start, my heart beating like a snare drum. I'd had a disturbing dream in which that awful image of Tod's skull kept surfacing again and again as I did the housework. Once it peered out at me from a basket of laundry, and another time it materialized in place of a jar of peanut butter. Awake and sweating, I lay completely still, that picture burned into my mind like a brand. How could I handle seeing it again, in front of the whole courtroom? If Rick were going to show that picture to anyone, I thought, he should be showing it to Tammy Wilson, Roger Cline, and Harry Joe Johnson so that it could haunt their dreams instead of mine.

At 7:00, Rog gently shook me awake. I was very groggy and wanted to be left alone. Somehow, by a supreme effort of will, I got up, took a shower, and struggled into some clothes. Catching a glimpse of myself in the bathroom mirror, I barely recognized myself. My face was pasty, and the skin under my eyes as dark as plums.

Bob and Rog tried to cheer me up, but even they could do nothing for me. "Don't worry, God will be with you," Jan answered. "He'll be holding your hand the whole time, just like he's holding Tod's right now."

That image made me feel a little better, and when we arrived at the courthouse at 8:45, I was more or less awake and back in control. I rolled the papers on which I had written the conversations into a tight scroll and squeezed it hard with both hands. If Tammy had been standing in front of me, I would have smashed it into her face like a club.

Finally the courtroom door opened, and I heard my name being called. I walked to the front of the room, where I was sworn in, and took my place in the witness chair sitting very straight, right on the edge of the chair. My knees began to shake as I continued squeezing the scroll of papers in my hands. Rick Lorensen must have sensed how nervous I was; he walked to the back of the room, giving me plenty of breathing room, then asked me my name. "Janet McQuaid."

"Mrs. McQuaid, how was Tod McQuaid related to you?"

My lips began to quiver. I paused, knowing my tears were ready to fall. After a while I said, "He was my son," in a soft voice.

"Do you know Tammy Wilson?"

"I met her once."

"Mrs. McQuaid, tell us how you know Tammy Wilson."

I explained Tod's visit to New York City in August for the alarm trade show, and the fact that he had brought Tammy along to learn about the alarm business. I went into great detail about the conversations she and I had in my living room, then her call in September, telling me Tod had had a heart attack. I explained every disturbing conversation we had had during the time he was supposed to be missing. As I looked at the jurors, I saw that some of them looked sympathetic, and I prayed that they were decent, honest people who could see Tammy Wilson for the fiend that she was. Gazing right at the jury, I told them about that terrible afternoon when Tammy called with the news that Tod had been found dead.

"Did Tammy Wilson sound upset and cry over the phone?"

"No, she was cold. She had a matter-of-fact attitude."

"Mrs. McQuaid, how did you know it was your son that was found?"

*Oh, no!* I thought. *This is where that awful picture comes in.* My hands began to tremble, but somehow I fought them under control. "By the gold and silver chains he wore around his neck."

"Your Honor," Rick said, "at this time I have a picture I would like to present to the witness as part of State's Exhibit 23."

Judge Jolliffe called the prosecutor and defense lawyer to the bench. There was a brief discussion, after which Judge Jolliffe made a decision to dismiss the jurors for five minutes. I wasn't sure what was gong on. Once the jury left the room, Rick Lorensen approached the witness chair with the picture in his hand and gave it to me. I held it low on my lap.

"Mrs. McQuaid, is this your son?"

I put my head down and half closed my eyes; I just couldn't bear to look at it again. Once was enough. I took a few deep breaths, trying to keep myself in control, and bit my lower lip, as I often did when I felt overwhelmed. Finally I nodded and quietly answered, "Yes, it's my son."

"How do you know it's your son?"

Again I paused. I wasn't sure I could give an answer without breaking down. If only I could keep my knees from shaking! How was I ever going to get through this? I lowered my head still further. "By the chains around his neck."

Rick took the picture from me and addressed the court.

"Your Honor, I would like to submit this as State's Exhibit 23."

Judge Jolliffe then addressed him. "Mr. Lorensen, that would mean that the jury would have access to the pictures during their deliberation, and I don't think that's something they need to see. The pictures the police had taken of Mr. McQuaid's body are totally gross and disgusting, with his body being so decayed and bugs all over him. The jury should be spared having to look at them."

He looked at me as if to observe my reactions, and at that moment all I could do was glare at him with horror and loathing. What did he mean, the jury should be spared? What about the hell I had just been put through having to look at that picture of my son's skull? What about the torture Tod had been put through? My heart was pounding, and I knew that if I didn't get out of that chair soon I was going to start ripping apart the entire courtroom.

The jury returned, and after they were seated, Rick said, "Thank you, Mrs. McQuaid, I have no further questions. Your witness."

Never getting up from his chair, Steve Hunter said, "No questions, your honor. I think Mrs. McQuaid has been through enough."

I walked out of the courtroom and staggered into the magazine room with Rog at my heels. I collapsed in a chair and wept. "What was the point in showing me that picture again?" I yelled at poor Rog. "The jury didn't even hear my answers regarding it. And the nerve of Jolliffe! Where in the hell was he coming from, making those cruel comments about Tod's decayed body?"

"Jan, please calm down!" Rog tried to take my hand, but I pulled it from his grasp. "Your blood pressure is going to shoot off the chart."

"You don't understand, do you?" I howled. "Why shouldn't the jurors have seen those pictures? That's part of their job. They need to see what those three bastards did to our son." The tears cascaded down my face like water.

Rog drew a deep breath and reached for my hand again. This time I let him take it. "Come with me," he said. We walked into the park and strolled among the flowerbeds. Just being in the presence of the brightly colored blossoms helped to ease my despair. Rog bought some containers of juice from a street vendor and handed one to me. "Have a sip," he encouraged me. "You're probably dehydrated. Feeling better now?"

I sipped slowly, relishing the tart taste of the lemonade. Then I paused and looked up at him, his image blurred by my tears. "Rog, why did they show me that horrible picture in the first place?"

Rog shrugged. "Perhaps Rick thought that the jury should see the pictures, too, and hoped that the judge would permit it. I guess that neither of them realized how it would affect you mentally, and me too, for that matter."

We had no sooner finished our drinks when the town clock struck noon: It was time to meet Bob and Jan. They were standing in the hall, and when Bob saw us he rushed up and clasped me in his arms like a bear. "You were so brave on that stand," he said.

"That's what you think," I murmured. "I was a bowl of pudding."

As much as I dreaded going back into that courtroom, I forced myself to go there; I had to talk to Rick. He and Steve Hunter were standing by their tables, both engaged in what seemed to be a deep conversation. As I made my way to the front, Rick saw me coming. "Fine job on the stand," he said, smiling.

"I would prefer we not discuss that," I said sternly. "I'm here to see about being in the courtroom this afternoon."

"I understand, but I can't give you an answer right now," he said, glancing at Hunter. "I'll check it out and let you know after lunch, okay?" He closed his briefcase and left the courtroom, apparently in a hurry to be out of my presence.

Rog, Bob, Jan and I went to a nearby bistro, tastefully decorated to look like a Parisian café, complete with impressive murals of the Eiffel Tower and the Left Bank. It was a relief getting away from the courthouse, if only for an hour. I needed that change of pace, and I surprised everyone when I ordered a vodka martini with lunch. "I deserve it," I said, enjoying every sip.

At 12:45 P.M. we were back in the courthouse hall, waiting. Rick came out of the elevator, saw me, and proceeded to walk toward me. I could hardly wait to hear what he had to say, but knew at once by his frown that it couldn't be good. "Mrs. McQuaid, I'm sorry, but it doesn't look promising. Steve isn't in favor of it, and he's going to give me his final answer very shortly. I expect that it will be no. I'm really sorry." With that, he turned and walked toward the courtroom doors.

I told Rog what Rick had said. "Who does this Hunter person

think he is, God? Why does he get to make all the decisions?"

Rog gave me a sympathetic look, as if to say, *I pity the poor bastard who has to stand up to you.* "I'm going to the library," he said at last, shaking his head. "Would you like to come along?"

"Soon, soon," I replied. "You go on. I'll catch up with you later." Feeling as if I were about to explode at any moment, I walked into the depressing little magazine room with its feeble lighting and gray furniture. I needed some time by myself, time to collect my thoughts and prepare myself for a rough afternoon. I was standing at the magazine table, flipping through a two-year-old issue of *Parents* Magazine, when I heard a male voice call my name. I turned around, expecting to find Rog or Rick or Bob. Steve Hunter was standing in the doorway. I stood with my hand on the magazine, glaring at him, never moving. High Noon, I thought.

"Mrs. McQuaid," Hunter said in a crisp, commanding voice. "Rick talked to me about your presence in the courtroom. I understand how much you want to be in there, and I'd like to allow you, but there's a problem. I might have to recall you to the stand."

What? Did he think I was stupid? He was the perfect lawyer for Tammy Wilson. Like her, I thought, he kept a straight face while hedging the truth. Looking at him right in the eye, I said, "Mr. Hunter, I'm sure you have your reasons for not wanting me to be in that courtroom, but you and I both know that recalling me is not a valid reason. I was not subpoenaed, you know. I testified as a friend of the court. And I clearly remember your statement when I was on the stand, 'No questions. I believe Mrs. McQuaid has been through enough.' You were absolutely right. I have been through enough. Now all I want is to see that woman and hear what she has to say. He was my son, Mr. Hunter. My son. I want to be there … for my son." I paused a moment, and I thought I saw a look of compassion flicker across his face like a shadow.

He was silent for several seconds, during which time he didn't seem to move at all. "Mrs. McQuaid, do you really want to be there in the courtroom to hear Tammy?" I nodded, my throat too tight to speak. Was this really happening, or had I misheard him? "Very well. I'll revisit the matter with Mr. Lorensen. We'll see if something can be arranged."

I nodded, too stupefied to say anything else. "Mr. Lorensen will be in touch with you. Mrs. McQuaid, I feel for you. I do." With that he turned and headed toward the courtroom.

Alone again, I gradually began to breathe normally. Slowly the tension began to slip from my body, and I looked down at my clenched hand, still resting on the magazine. I looked at the empty doorway. "Thank you," I whispered.

I told Rog about my chance meeting with Hunter and his startling offer of cooperation. Rog thought it was a good sign, but he wasn't convinced that Hunter would come through for us. Cracking open Bob's notebook, I delved back into the testimony.

The next witness Rick Lorensen called to the stand was Sandy Echols, Roger Cline's mother. She testified that, on October 6th, Roger had driven a company car — "I can't tell you if it was a dark blue Blazer or what" — to her home and showed it to her. He pointed out the telephone inside it and the guards' scheduling chart, very proud of himself and not at all nervous. "There was a carpet lying in the back, all rolled up, and I asked Roger, 'What is that carpet doing back there?' and he said, 'It's just an old carpet I have got to get rid of.' I thought nothing more about it." She said that he was on his way to Ohio to visit his brother. Tammy had called him there, and Roger had made a call to Tammy.

Reading Mrs. Echols testimony boggled my mind. What kind of monster was this Roger Cline? Why did he drive to his mother's house with Tod's body rolled up in a carpet, and then have her look into the Bronco with the body in the back? It sounded like something from a horror movie. The more I knew about this case and the three murderers, the less I thought of the whole human race.

# CHAPTER SIXTEEN

It was another beautiful sunny day, but I was hardly aware of the lovely weather as we drove to the courthouse. Rog and I greeted Rick Lorensen on the courthouse steps before going inside, knowing what our day would be like. Rick wasn't in the best of moods. He seemed to be annoyed. It seems that Judge Jolliffe had granted permission to delay Roger's testimony for a short time so that his lawyer, Paul Detch, could prepare him for the stand.

Rick explained that, instead of Roger Cline taking the stand this morning, a videotape of the testimony of two witnesses, William S. Coleman, the owner of Coleman's Pharmacy in Lewisburg, and Dr. James Vascik, had been made and was going to be shown to the jurors. We didn't get a chance to see it, but somehow Bob got a copy of the transcript so I could read it. Although I wanted to ask Rick if he had spoken to Mr. Hunter about allowing me into the courtroom, I decided to wait: Rick looked as if he were about to burst into flames, and I certainly didn't want to ignite him.

I sat down with the transcript on a bench in the main hallway and began poring over the pages. Mr. Coleman's testimony came first, and Rick was the first to question him. Mr. Coleman said that he had filled a prescription on September 21 in the name of Tammy Wilson, for twelve valium tablets, ten milligrams. It was written by Dr. James M. Vasick of Roanoke, Virginia.

"Mr. Coleman, do you recall who came in to have the prescription filled?"

"Not vividly. It was a young man of medium build, with a mustache. I'm not positive that I could actually identify him again. I remember the mustache and I remember the man's thin build. His hair was medium brown."

Rick passed the witness to Steve Hunter. "Bill, there's a young lady seated to my left. Do you know who she is?"

"No, I do not."

"The person that you tendered these twelve valium tablets to, did he give you an address?"

"He said, 'It's right down over the hill.' He gave the name of the street as North Jefferson."

In reading this, I couldn't understand why the prosecutor or defense didn't ask Mr. Coleman if he knew Tod. I was not about to leave any stones unturned and, after finishing that part of the transcript, took it upon myself to call Mr. Coleman. He expressed his sympathy and talked about Tod stopping in the pharmacy from time to time, just to say hello and talk a little. "Yes, I knew Tod. It definitely was not Tod who had that valium prescription filled," Mr. Coleman said.

The description he gave fit Harry Joe Johnson. Did Harry Joe Johnson lie on the stand, saying he didn't have the prescription filled? In my opinion, I think he did, and I think the prosecutor and defense knew it too. I returned to the transcript. Dr. James Vascik's videotape was shown next. Rick Lorensen, Steve Hunter, and Tammy Wilson were also on the tape.

Mr. Lorensen began the questioning by asking the doctor to identify a written prescription.

"It looks like my signature," Dr. Vascik said. "I can compare it to a copy. Yes, that looks to appear to be my prescription." When Mr. Lorensen asked the doctor if there were any discrepancies in the prescription, versus the copy of the original, Dr. Vascik said that there were. "The copy says, dispense two in number, the number two in parentheses. The number one has been written in front of the two, apparently changing the number to twelve."

The doctor recalled that he had seen Tammy Wilson in his office around September 20th, complaining of a numbing sensation in her left cheek after an automobile accident.

"The person who presented herself to you as Tammy Wilson .... Do you have any other records concerning her which would identify her as this person?"

"Other than her age, twenty-nine, and weight, one forty-three. She's five foot seven. I have no other identifying data."

Mr. Hunter cross-examined. "Dr. Vascik, is there anything else on your prescription that's been changed or altered, other than the number of tablets to be dispensed?"

"The refill zero has been circled; it wasn't on the original. Her address has been added, I assume by the pharmacist. That appears to be it; plus, the pharmacist has put a copy of his label from the bottle on the prescription, which is pretty usual."

I finished reading just as the courtroom doors opened, and Rog was summoned inside. This was not the morning for the magazine room or the library. I sat and waited in the hall. Rog seemed to be on the stand an awfully long time. Finally, Rog walked out of the courtroom, along with Bob and Jan. Rog didn't seem overjoyed when I asked, "How did it go?" He just shook his head and told me that, before he left the courtroom, he had spoken to Rick. " 'No firm decision has been reached as of yet,' " Rog said, quoting the lawyer.

After lunch, it was my turn to suggest we sit in the garden for a while. Rog was as tense as a bowstring, and I hoped that he wouldn't come in contact with Steve Hunter for a while; the defense lawyer, it seems, had been pretty ruthless with poor Rog, although he refused to go into any details. Bob handed me his notes from the morning session just before he and Jan headed back into the courtroom. Rog and I sat outside for over an hour, and eventually he began to relax, just a little, amid the joyous roses and lilies. Rog supported the local vendor, this time buying ice-cold bottles of exotic juice blends, although he told me that he would have preferred Cutty Sark, straight up. Rog rarely drank hard liquor, so I knew that he must have been under intense pressure.

When we finished our juice, we returned to the courthouse and entered the library. Rog took yet another law volume from the shelf, while I opened Bob's notebook and eagerly began reading my husband's testimony. What had happened to upset this steadiest, most cool-headed of men?

Mr. Lorensen asked Rog when he first became aware of Tod's status.

"The missing status was on Monday, October 15th, 1990. We were in Pittsburgh when Jan, my wife, received a phone call from Tammy Wilson, announcing that Tod was dead, and Jan told me."

"Let me hand you what is marked as State's Exhibit No. 35 and ask if that is a picture of your son when he was living?" (Rick had asked us for a picture of Tod earlier, so the jurors could see it.)

"Yes, it is. This is a picture of Tod at his wedding in New Jersey."

"Mr. McQuaid, when did your son move to West Virginia?"

"September of 1983, I believe." Rog went on to describe Tod's guard and alarm businesses in great detail, which made me smile. Then it was Mr. Hunter's turn to cross-examine Rog.

"Mr. McQuaid, have you been living in Lewisburg the full time since October 1990?"

"Since October 25th I have been commuting from New Jersey to Lewisburg on an average of once a week. I have what I call a 'straw boss' who assists me, and if problems occur, I step in to try to resolve them."

"Regarding the office building, was the rent paid current on that building at the time you took over the business, sir?"

"Yes, it was."

I recalled one of the statements Tammy had given, saying that Tod was behind several months in his rent. There may have been a method behind Mr. Hunter's madness in asking this question, but it was just another one of Tammy's lies. And it backfired.

"Mr. McQuaid, were there any personal expenditures that Tammy Wilson took out of the TEMAC accounts for the period of October 6th and October 25th, when you took over?"

"Yes. TEMAC Century had a number of personal checks. One was to pay the insurance for Mick Morgan, Tammy Wilson's father. There were a number of those type of payments out of that checking account."

"Mr. McQuaid, let me hand you what has been marked as State's Exhibit No. 36 and ask you to review that check, please. This is a check drawn on TEMAC, Inc., Atlantic Financial of Lewisburg, West Virginia, made out for two hundred eighty four dollars and fifty cents, to Mountain State Carpet, with a signature of Tod McQuaid. Now, let me hand you what has been marked as Exhibit No. 37 and ask if you can identify that document."

"Yes. This is a contract, a floor covering proposal, customer name, Todd McQuaid, with two d's, not my son's name. The phone number is 645-4600, the TEMAC guard telephone number. Tammy Wilson's name is beside the phone number. It was paid in full on 10-8-90. There wasn't any new flooring at the TEMAC office."

"That's all."

Mr. Lorensen began to re-examine. "Mr. McQuaid, were there any expenditures on a Visa card for TEMAC, Inc.?"

"Yes, there were. I have a Visa statement from November of 1990 that shows that on October 9th, 1990, a transaction occurred with U.S. Air for about five hundred seventy dollars. The specific document does not indicate the name of the person whom the ticket is for. I found that it was not for a TEMAC purpose. Obviously, with a date of October 9th, it raised the possibility of being an illegal expenditure. Therefore, I researched the information and was able to get a reversal on that charge."

"What is your understanding of the date of Tod's death?"

"October 6th, 1990."

"Between October 6th and October 26th, 1990, did you have a policy concerning expenditures of his accounts?"

"Yes. I would challenge the validity of any of those expenditures, since Tod was not present to execute expenditures."

It was now Mr. Hunter's turn to re-examine Rog. "The prosecutor questioned you about the purchase at Mountain State Carpets. He asked you everything on there except one thing. I will hand you what was marked Exhibit No. 37 and ask you to look at the top of that invoice and tell us what the purchase date was."

"The date of the order was 10-4-90."

"Thank you, sir. That's all I have, your Honor."

"That date that it was paid for was, again, what date?" Mr. Lorensen asked on re-direct.

"The date paid was 10-8-90."

"Mr. McQuaid, who signed the check? Whose name appears?"

"Tod McQuaid's name appears."

"Mr. McQuaid, can you recognize that as his signature?"

"In my opinion, it is not Tod McQuaid's. I am very familiar with my son's signature, and I know that the check was not written by my son."

Rog thought his testimony was insignificant and a total waste of time, which made him angry, and he had not cared at all for Mr. Hunter's brusque attitude. Of course, being kept out of the courtroom after we testified didn't help matters.

I went on reading that morning's testimony.

Michael Hess, who was employed by the deputy sheriff's office in Belmont county, Ohio, was next to be called to the stand. He testified that he had received a call at 3:37 A.M. on the 23rd of October by the dispatcher, who had talked with a Cathy Cline who had called in about the location of a body. He and another deputy went to the location in York Township and discovered the body. They had called for a supervisor and for a coroner investigator. When they arrived, they called for lathing equipment from the local fire department because the body was in a heavily wooded area surrounded by a steep gorge. The gorge ultimately led down to a dry creek bed, and it had been very difficult to get the body out of the remote area.

As I read all this, the reality of the entire situation still seemed unbelievable to me.

The next morning, as we got off the elevator, I noticed a very tall man sitting in one of the chairs against the wall. I recognized him, and before I had the opportunity to say hello, the courtroom doors were flung open wide and he entered. It was Dr. Sopher, Chief Medical Examiner for the state of West Virginia. He had received Tod's body on October 23rd, 1990, and performed the autopsy.

Seeing him again made me think of the time I had called Dr. Sopher. It was a few days after Tod's death, and it wasn't easy for me to pull myself together enough to make that call. Introducing myself as the mother of Tod McQuaid, I explained that I had a few questions I needed to have answered in order to help put my mind at ease, and he agreed to help me any way he could. I asked him what Tod had been wearing, and the doctor replied that Tod was wearing only a pair of blue jockey shorts. When I asked him if Tod was wearing any jewelry, he mentioned the two neck-chains, one gold, one silver.

"Was he wearing any rings?" Dr. Sopher said that he was not. Tod had a beautiful, man's diamond ring that he wore whenever he dressed in a suit. Since Tammy had staged the TEMAC break-in, there was no doubt in my mind that she had stolen that ring.

"Dr. Sopher, what about drugs?" I asked. "Did you find any drugs in Tod's body?"

"Ma'am, your son didn't have any drugs in his body. There was some alcohol found, but no drugs."

That was the end of my call, but it turned out that our dealings with Dr. Sopher were far from over. On a trip to Lewisburg just before the Wilson trial, we stopped in the prosecutor's office to find out how things were progressing. As we sat and talked with Rick, he explained he was having problems and that time was limited, so he asked if we would be willing to help him. "What sort of help?" Rog had asked.

Rick replied that the state police had done an outstanding job on the investigation, but he wasn't satisfied with the autopsy report from Dr. Sopher. Harry Joe Johnson had stated that Tammy Wilson had given Tod a drug to knock him out, and the evidence pointed to the valium prescription. Since Tammy had inserted a one in front of the doctor's two on the prescription label, allowing her to receive twelve valium tablets, it could only be assumed that she had given Tod the valium in alcohol. Dr. Sopher's report didn't mention finding valium, so Rick asked if we would do some research on valium for him.

Rog and I were taken by surprise at his request, but wanting to see Tammy Wilson spend the rest of her life in prison was such a strong incentive that we agreed to help. Once we were outside Rick's office, I asked Rog, "Why do you suppose he asked us to get involved in this research?"

"Jan, your guess is as good as mine, but if it will hang her, let's do it," he replied.

My immediate thought was to contact my cousin Pam, who was involved in medical research. I explained our dilemma to Pam, and her first question was, "Did he examine the liver?"

We didn't know. Pam, who was more than willing to gather information for us, gave us the title of a book that dealt with valium. She suggested that her brother Mark could also help us and told us to contact him for additional information. These two were the answer to our prayers. Mark and Pam sent us valuable information that we passed along to Rick. Then we questioned Dr. Sopher, who admitted that he had only tested Tod's urine for drugs. With clinical information in hand, we asked him to consider doing another autopsy, this time examining the liver and kidneys, not just the urine.

Dr. Sopher was more than willing to accommodate us, although he explained that there wasn't much blood in Tod's body for a large amount of testing. Fortunately, he did perform a second autopsy. Dr. Sopher explained that, during the second procedure, he was able to retrieve valium from samples of Tod's urine, liver, and kidney tissue that had been saved.

There was still the big question: How much valium Tammy had given Tod to knock him out? Besides the valium and alcohol, what else might she have given him? However, these would become just more questions we would never be able to answer. It didn't make me any less grateful to Pam and Mark, or to Dr. Sopher.

Shaking myself out of my reverie, I decided to go to the magazine room to read Bob's notes, which detailed the testimony of Roger Cline. Roger was twenty-six years old and had graduated from high school by taking special education classes. He claimed he was slow. His uncle was married to Tammy's mother, and it was Tammy who had hired him to be a handy man around the TEMAC office. When asked to recall the night of September 22nd, Roger explained that Tammy had him break mirrors and damage other items in the TEMAC office, then take some furnishings to her house. He thought she was playing a joke on Evelyn Gettman, and that it was just a prank.

Roger Cline stated that in September Tammy asked him to "knock off" her ex-husband for ten thousand dollars in an attempt to get her girls back, but Roger refused her offer. He claimed that about two months before Tod's death, she started talking about knocking off Tod because she wanted to take over his business.

I immediately recalled that dinner together in August. Could it be that Tammy had been starting to put her plan into operation when I met her? That's why she had made such a fuss over her story about the TEMAC break-in. I became irate when Roger stated that Tammy told him that Tod molested his girls, and that he had struck her. In return for killing Tod, Tammy offered him part ownership and a truck and a lifetime job for his brother.

Roger explained how Tammy planned the whole thing and got everything arranged, down to getting him the office keys and everything else they needed, including the guns. Harry Joe Johnson, Roger and Tammy had several meetings at Tammy's house to plan how they would kill Tod. Tammy was going to take care of getting him drugged and knocked out so that he couldn't defend himself. The date was set for October 5th. Once Roger and Harry Joe had everything collected from the TEMAC office, they drove by Tammy's house to see if Tod was walking around. Roger said he thought he saw Tammy dragging something. They drove to a store and called the house, and Tammy told them that "Tod was ready and laying on the floor knocked out."

When Roger and Harry entered the house, Tammy was standing with a gun in her hand. Roger claims he snapped. He went into the bedroom where Tod was lying on his right side, with his back toward him, and fired three shots with a .40 caliber, missing him. He said Tod never moved.

Tammy thought there were blanks in the gun. She and Roger got into an argument, and it was then that she ordered Roger to shoot Tod in the back of the head. She stated that if he didn't shoot Tod, she was going to kill one of his family members, perhaps his little girl. When Roger fired again and missed, Tammy threatened to kill his uncle or even her own mother to get what she wanted. She handed Roger a .45 caliber and once again threatened him, saying that she was going to shoot him if he failed. Roger said that he then fired the gun and hit Tod in the back of the head.

Roger explained about Harry Joe wrapping up the body and helping Roger place it in the Bronco. Tammy didn't want the body in West Virginia, so Roger drove the body to Ohio near a spot where couples parked on weekends. He dragged Tod over the hill, threw a few rocks on him and left. Then he visited his mother and drove back to Lewisburg Sunday night. Tammy made him spend the night at the TEMAC office, not wanting him out of her sight. When he woke up in the morning, Harry Joe was standing over him with a gun in his hand, and Tammy grabbed hold of him and said, "Not yet." That scared Roger. Tammy had told him that, if he talked with the police, she would start killing off his family. He walked into the TEMAC office one morning and overheard Tammy talking on the phone, saying, "Roger's next."

On the night of October 23rd, Roger told his uncle everything that had happened. He was scared and, under his uncle's urging, he turned himself into the police.

I had to set down the notebook for a few moments because my fingers were quivering so badly. It felt as if they had been burned just by coming in contact with those pages. God in heaven, I thought, the jurors had to see what an evil person Tammy Wilson was.

I resumed reading. Roger claimed that it wasn't until the murder was over that Tammy became hysterical and started bawling. He felt Tammy took advantage of him because he was slow and that she liked to play with people's minds. He was afraid of her and said, "She just had a look in her eyes" that he couldn't explain. It was interesting he would say that, since I had felt the same coldness in her expression when she sat in our living room that August.

Roger went on to say that he had made up the story about being the sole person involved because of Tammy's threat to kill his family. He thought that if he went to jail for the crime without involving Tammy and Harry Joe, she would leave everyone else alone. He said that she called it "the perfect crime."

I closed the notebook. Tomorrow Tammy Wilson would take the stand, and we would see how "perfectly" she behaved. I wondered how dramatic she might become. Would she cry? Would she try to come across like an innocent schoolgirl? Whatever tricks she tried to pull, I was one-hundred-percent certain that she would lie her way through her testimony. I was contemplating simply walking into the courtroom and taking my chances, when I remembered what Steve Hunter had promised, or seemed to have promised. I still hadn't heard whether I was in or out.

# CHAPTER SEVENTEEN

What seemed like the longest week of my life was coming to a close. I kept praying to God to guide the jurors in the right direction, and as far as I was concerned, that direction was "Guilty in the First Degree with No Mercy."

When we arrived at the courthouse, I was just about to enter when Rick rushed up behind us and laid his hand on my arm. I turned to see his face plastered with a huge smile. "Hunter called me this morning," he panted, still grinning. "Guess what? You're in!"

"Amen," Rog muttered, glancing upward. "Miracles do happen."

I was so excited that I could barely squeak out a reply. "Really? You're sure?"

Rick nodded as he took my elbow and guided me into courthouse. Rog, Bob and Jan were right behind us. "Yes, yes. And you'll both be present for closing arguments. Of course, Mr. Hunter has a few stipulations about today's arrangements. First of all, only you, Mrs. McQuaid, may attend, and you must sit as far back in the courtroom as possible, as far removed from the jury as you can get. You mustn't say anything or do anything to draw attention to yourself. If you don't behave yourself, Steve will have you out of there faster than Secretariat with a burr under his saddle."

Of course after Rick said that I was in, I barely heard another word he said. If it meant that I would have to stand on my head during all of Tammy's testimony, I would have been all too happy to do so. Promising that he would send someone for us later, Rick rushed off toward the courtroom.

People were milling around in the hall like so many sheep in need of a border collie. Rog nodded toward benches, and when I looked in that direction I saw Sergeants Johnson and Sloan, sitting awkwardly in the wooden seats. As I walked over to say good morning to them, I noticed a man and a young boy approximately fifteen years of age sitting along the wall. Knowing that Tammy had been married three times, I wondered if this was her first husband and their son. I had met her second husband and knew it wasn't him.

At 8:50, everyone began making their way into the courtroom ... all but the man and boy, who continued to sit against the wall. I thought that their behavior was rather strange. If they weren't going to attend the trial, what were they doing there? To make matters worse, I wasn't sure what I should do, either, if I should go in by myself, or wait for the person Rick has promised to send. I was standing at the doors, trying to decide, when a broadly-built, handsome young black gentleman in an elegant pinstriped suit came up to me and smiled warmly. "Mrs. McQuaid?" he said, extending his hand. I nodded. "Pleased to meet you. I'm Tyler Williams. Mr. Lorensen sent me to escort you. Won't you come with me, please?"

Trembling with nervous energy, I hugged Rog goodbye and allowed Tyler to guide me into the courtroom. We sat in the back row, as far from the jury as possible, and I knew that it would be difficult indeed for any of them to see me, screened as I was by this nice young man's sizeable bulk. I looked around, but couldn't see Bob and Jan, although I knew that they must be seated already. Giant butterflies the size of baseball gloves began fluttering in my stomach.

I began looking for Tammy, but all I could see was the back of her head and occasional glimpses of her profile. I felt angry and excited and strangely happy, all at once. After all, at least I was going to get a chance to see this woman's performance for myself. I prayed she would tie herself into a knot with her lies, but what if she managed to deceive the jury, just as she had deceived everyone else, myself included? Like an Olympic athlete, she was at the top of her game when it came to lying.

I was lost in my thoughts, and before I knew what was happening, Mr. Hunter called Tammy to the stand and started the interrogation. I stared straight at her, barely able to breathe. In her demure gray suit with blue blouse and matching floral-patterned scarf, she looked as if she were trying to portray someone incapable of murder. "Would you state your name, please?"

"Tammy Sherrell Wilson," she said, in a confident voice.

"Tammy, are you the person who was charged in an indictment, along with Harry Joe Johnson and Roger E. Cline, with the murder of Tod McQuaid?"

"Yes, I was."

"Have you previously entered a plea of not guilty?"

"Yes, I have."

"When were you first employed by Tod McQuaid or the corporate entity of TEMAC, Incorporated?"

"It was back in July of 1990. The employment office sent me there for a security guard position. I worked in that position for three days; then Tod put me into the office, and I mostly answered the telephones for about two days. He told me he needed an operations manager to handle interviews, the beginning interviews, before he did the final one to weed out people he didn't want. He had TEMAC Security Alarms. That was his original business. He bought TEMAC Guard when he moved down here, and had around thirty to forty clients."

"Tammy, prior to and after you went to work for Tod, there has been testimony that you and he developed a relationship; is that correct?"

"Well, I guess it happened right from the beginning. The first night I was on the job he kept showing up to watch me. Eventually, after about six days, we were inseparable. He was either at the house on Coffman Hill or we were in the office. In essence, we were living together."

"When was Roger Cline employed?"

"It was around the time of the state fair, sometime in August. Tod worked in the Chicken Shack for the Rotary, because he belonged to the Rotary Club. He tried to go there at least every day."

"Did Tod employ an accountant or bookkeeper?"

"Yes. Tod didn't let anybody handle the company books but him and his accountant."

"Do you recall when Harry Joe Johnson was employed?"

"I believe it was the first or second week of September. At the time, Tod decided he wanted to spend more time with me, and he wanted to spend more time with his family because he hadn't been near them. He wanted somebody to help him with the alarm business and ran short in the security guard business, so he had Harry doing that."

"Tammy, you have heard Roger Cline testify and heard the statement read that you had given to trooper Tom Johnson. Did you ever have any conversation with Harry Joe Johnson about killing Tod McQuaid?"

"I didn't."

"Did you ever have a conversation with Roger Cline involving the death of your former husband?"

"Yes. Roger took turns working my Coffman Hill house and the TEMAC office. Tod would send me out or he would go out and check on Roger when he was working because Roger had a tendency to drink on the job or be lazy. I went out to check on him once, and the subject of Roger's little girl and my children had come up. Roger had brought that up. He said he had killed a guy named Kenny Baker for his wife, and this was a good way to get rid of problems. I said to him, 'Don't talk crazy.' "

(I just managed to avoid rolling my eyes when she said this. As far as I was concerned, she was the craziest woman in the state.)

"There has been testimony that there was a meeting at your house involving Harry Joe Johnson and Roger Cline. Do you recall any such meeting?"

"There was no such meeting."

"Are you saying that you never met and discussed with Harry Joe Johnson and Roger Cline the killing of Tod McQuaid?"

"I certainly did not. I was in love with Tod."

(Tod in love with Tammy. Now there was a ridiculous idea. If only the jury could see through her deceit.)

"Where do you think they got this notion about the meeting?"

"Only if she knows, your honor," Rick said, interrupting Mr. Hunter.

Judge Jolliffe looked at Mr. Hunter thoughtfully. "The answer can't be speculation," he said. "If she has information with respect to the question, she can testify, but only in that case."

"Tammy, do you have information on why Harry testified like this?" Mr. Hunter asked carefully.

"They practiced stories, I mean, before they turned themselves in," Tammy said coolly, without the slightest trace of nerves. "They used to talk about who shot Tod and blame each other. I overheard them more than once."

(Oh, she was good!)

"Were you in the house the night that they shot him?"

"Yes, I was. We worked really late that night, probably until 9:00. Keith Coffman had stopped in the TEMAC office and stayed until 9:15. Then we went to the Fort Savannah to have a drink and relax."

"How much did Tod have to drink there?"

"Probably two scotch and waters and one blackberry brandy. Then we went back to the TEMAC office to put all the radios and clipboards and things into the lock box for the guard that would be coming on duty around 11:00 P.M."

"Tammy, let's move on to the night Tod was killed. What time do you recall that you got your first call from Roger Cline?"

"It must have been around 12:00 or 12:30. Tod bought some rice and carrots and stuff and made Chinese food. We were on a different schedule than other people. The alarm business was a night-time thing, and we sometimes would sleep later in the morning."

I stared at Tammy in disbelief. It was only by the grace of God that I was able to keep from crying out, "She's lying!" The alarm business wasn't a night-time business. There were exceptions, and sometimes alarms had to be installed at night, but those instances were few and far between. As for the guard business, she had no idea when he purchased it. It wasn't when he first moved down to Lewisburg, but early in 1990. It made my blood boil that she could keep manufacturing lies and get away with them.

"So, Tammy, you went home and ate. Did you have anything to drink?" Mr. Hunter asked.

"Yes, sir, I believe I had some wine coolers. Tod had red-eyes, that's beer and tomato juice. I don't think he had more than three, but I probably drank a little bit too much that night."

"Now, what did Roger call you about?"

"Tod and Roger had talked about Roger's father's junkyard in Ohio, because Tod needed an engine in one of the Broncos. He had given Roger three hundred dollars to go up there and get an engine, and Roger had Tod's permission to take the blue Bronco to Ohio that Friday night. Roger called us because Tod had forgotten to leave the insurance card in the lockbox, and Roger needed it before he could make the trip. Roger had a driver's license to permit him to drive to and from work. Tod had to sign a paper saying it was work-related because Roger had a DUI. I told Tod what Roger had forgotten, and Tod made some gesture or something. We waited for Roger, but he never did show up, so we went into the bedroom. Tod received a communication call on his phone radio. He left it on all night for incoming emergency calls, and I answered it. It was Roger. He said he was going to be there in a minute.

"Shortly afterwards I heard somebody come through the kitchen, and I grabbed my big shirt and put it on. I got up and walked towards the dining room, and that's when I saw Roger. I didn't see Harry Joe Johnson at first. Roger he pushed me aside, and then I saw Harry. He said, 'Stand still' and held me down. I heard two shots. Harry Joe told me to shut up because I was screaming too loud. I remember standing up, and I was shaking. I needed to get to Tod, and Harry said, 'You don't want to go in there. You can't go in there.' I went into the dining room and Harry pushed me down in the corner, and that's when I saw Roger come out of the bedroom. Harry went to the bedroom. I got as far as the stove in the living room and Harry came out and pushed me back down and hollered, 'Hey, Roger.' Roger had backed the Bronco up to the back door and they talked about something. Roger turned around and said, 'Now you do it.' Harry goes, 'I'm just the clean-up man, I'm not having no part in hurting any woman.' That's really all I heard. Then Roger all of a sudden grabbed Harry's gun and went to the bedroom door and shot again."

"Did you ever see Tod McQuaid?"

"After the third shot, the door opened, and I could see his feet, that's all. Harry Joe was telling me to shut up because I was crying and screaming."

"Did you do anything else?"

"I really don't know. I know one time I got out to the yard, but most of the time he kept me in the corner of the dining room."

"Tammy, until you heard Dr. Sopher testify, did you really know how Tod McQuaid died?"

"I had come to a conclusion from the gory stories that Roger and Harry tormented me with the next week, but they never told me they shot him in the head. They always told me he had been shot in the chest and they poured acid all over his body, that he didn't die for three or four days, and they had him in a cave. That was what Harry Joe told me."

"What about Rachel Johnson?"

"She moved into the TEMAC office on Saturday morning and never left. She and Harry moved right in and never left me."

(Huh! I thought. We know who the real prisoner was, and Tammy, it wasn't you!)

"Do you remember when the police called you?"

For the first time that morning, Tammy looked a tiny bit rattled as she brushed a lock of hair away from her face. "I called them first. Then I called Mrs. McQuaid and asked her some questions, because Harry and Roger led me to believe that maybe Tod was just hurt. Then on the night of October 15th, I'm not quite sure of the date, I called Trooper Johnson at least three times a day from that day until they arrested me. In the beginning, when I told them about the phone call, they needed to look for Tod, somebody needed to. There were three guns at the time that were on top of the mantle over the fireplace, which you could see from the TEMAC office. Trooper Johnson came in, and I pointed to Tod's three guns, telling him that Tod McQuaid didn't go anywhere without one of them. His vehicles were all there, and his driver's license, and his daily planner. He had not missed a day writing in the daily planner for the last ten years. The last date he wrote in it was October 5th, and I gave all of this to Trooper Johnson. His reply was, 'I have checked into things a little bit, Tammy, and I know what kind of person Tod McQuaid is. This is probably the way he played it. It's a stunt of some kind for Tod to get publicity for his business."

"Who said that to you?"

(Man, this woman likes to walk on thin ice, I thought. She was even willing to lie about the police. It was as if she were composing a novel, right there on the witness stand!)

"Tom Johnson. I met him before I started working at TEMAC. I also knew some other officers."

"Tammy, why didn't you call the police earlier?"

According to Tammy, Roger and Harry threatened her kids. They told her there was a third person involved in the crime and he was watching her family. She said that Roger claimed he had killed once before and he could do it again. It was Harry that mostly threatened her. It was always Roger that was going to do it, never Harry, or this third person.

(This woman has been watching too much television if she thinks that the jury is going to fall for this story. At least, I hoped I was right.)

"When did you first learn somebody had confessed to Tod McQuaid's murder?" Mr. Hunter asked.

Tammy said that on the night of the 23rd, her mother called and said she had something horrible to tell her. Tammy said she already knew what it was, and asked her mother if Roger had told her what he had done. Her mother replied that he had told her everything and for some reason was scared of Harry Joe Johnson, because Roger thought Harry was going to kill his little girl. Tammy said she was glad he was going to the police to turn himself in, and when she got off the phone, she told Harry Joe and Rachel what she had told her mother. The next morning, she said, she called the state police and told them what she knew about the murder.

"How long did it take them to take the statement on the 24th of October, after you had been arrested?" Mr. Hunter asked.

"I had three conversations with the police — one at the TEMAC office, one in the trooper's car, and then when we got to the state trooper's office," Tammy said carefully. "He had just gotten a statement from Harry Johnson and asked me some questions. I went to jail the next day."

"Had you seen any bullet holes in the floor?"

"No, not until I was released in your custody and taken to my house."

"Tammy, in the statement you gave Trooper Johnson, he testified that you said the motivation for killing Tod was the following: 'Tod had touched my daughter under six years of age, while she was bathing at the TEMAC office on Sunday of the weekend before October 6th, 1990.' Did you say that?"

Tammy made a quick, flipping gesture with her hand. It seemed to me as if she were manually trying to rearrange her testimony. "That's not the way ... that question was not directed toward me. Trooper Johnson said he couldn't figure out what the motive was. He said stuff like, 'What was the motive, why would they do this?' I said, 'I don't know, they never discussed it.' The only thing Roger at one time did bring up was that Tod supposedly did something like that to my daughter. He said, 'That's why Tod didn't get to see his little girls in New Jersey,' which I knew was a lie, because he had seen them, but I still went and called Rose about that."

"You told the State Troopers, 'I don't know why Harry got involved. I think we are all crazy. How could we do this? I didn't think Roger or I thought we would go through with it, and I can't figure why Harry got involved.' Did you make that statement?"

Tammy, although committing herself to a huge lie, looked completely unfazed. "Part of it. Trooper Johnson kept asking me why Harry got involved, and I couldn't answer why he did what he did. Harry was never supposed to go with Roger to get the Bronco engine in Ohio. I had made a reservation for Harry and his wife's anniversary the next day, so there was no reason, like I told Trooper Johnson. He asked me if I thought Roger and Harry were crazy, and I said, 'I think we are all crazy, because we have to live with what happened.' I was trying to protect my kids, my family. I didn't know if there was somebody else out there. I knew these people were dangerous. I was there, I saw blood all over Harry."

"Now the statement, 'I didn't think we would go through with this ....' What are you referring to there?"

"I don't remember making that statement."

"Tammy, did you ask Roger Cline to kill Tod McQuaid and promise him any part of the business?"

"I did not."

"Well, did you think you owned some part of the business?"

"Nobody owned any part of the business but Tod."

(Well, at least that was the truth, I thought, even if she didn't believe it.)

"Did you give Tod McQuaid any alcohol or drugs in order to render him unconscious?"

"I never gave Tod anything to drink, and I didn't give him any drugs and I didn't hit him with anything, and I didn't do anything to render him unconscious."

"Tammy, you know, after he had been killed, you did not call the police that night. Correct?"

"I didn't really know Tod was dead, probably until the 15th. I had to get the police involved, and they didn't get involved until I called them every day for a long time. They believed it was a game until Roger turned himself in."

"Did you know what kind of money they were making there at the business?"

"Somewhat. Not really. It was something Tod kept private and handled with his accountant."

"Do you know where the bank accounts were?"

"Yes, but I didn't know where Tod's personal account was."

"Tammy, from the time Tod was killed until the time you were arrested, did you, in fact, run the business?"

"Yes, except for the first couple of days, when Harry and Rachel were really mean to me."

"Thank you, Tammy, I have no further questions at this time."

As Rick Lorensen walked up to the stand to begin his cross-examination, I silently prayed for him to be as sharp and ruthless as I knew he could be. "You said that you had a conversation with Roger Cline about killing your ex-husband; is that correct?" Rick began.

Tammy made a restless little shrug. "Well, I wouldn't call it a conversation. Roger made a statement to me, a suggestion, something like that."

"Did you give him encouragement or say you wanted to have your ex-husband killed to get custody of your children?"

"Of course not."

"Roger Cline stated you offered him ten thousand dollars to kill your ex-husband. How long did you know Roger?"

"Probably met him the day before he started to work at the TEMAC office, the same time Tod McQuaid met him. My mom mentioned to me that Roger needed a job, and Tod needed odds and ends done. Tod felt sorry for certain people, and he would give them extra jobs and things to do."

"You said that there had been a burglar alarm at the TEMAC office, a pretty fancy one?"

"To me it seemed like it was. When Tod first got the building, he got special permission to put it in from the owner."

"You said Evelyn Gettman broke into the building. How did she break in if there was a burglar alarm?"

"I can't answer that."

"Do you recall the evidence of Mrs. McQuaid?" he said, and my ears perked up. I pulled a handkerchief from my cardigan pocket and balled it into my fist.

"Somewhat."

"Do you recall her saying that when she met you, you talked about Evelyn Gettman making a threat to Tod? Did you tell her that?"

"Yes, sir."

"You called Mrs. McQuaid and told her Tod had a heart attack, didn't you?"

"I called Tod McQuaid's mother and told her that Tod had complained of chest pains. He wasn't the type of person that would tell you anything if he was sick. I thought maybe he was sick and so I called his mother, to talk to her, just to see about Tod's past health."

"Do you recall Mrs.McQuaid saying this phone call took place on September 21st?"

"I'm not sure. I made two phone calls to her, one before Tod died and one after."

(Two phone calls! Preposterous! Our phone bill was over $400.)

"When did Rachel Johnson start working for TEMAC?"

"Rachel never worked at TEMAC. She came in my house and told me what to do when nobody was around. She carried a gun around with her all the time."

"When did this start?"

"October 6th."

"Ms. Wilson, you said Roger Cline had a driver's license. Then you said he didn't have a driver's license, but he could get authorization from an employer to drive to and from work. On what law was that based?"

"I have no idea. That wasn't part of my job there. That's why Tod signed special forms for him whenever he drove over to Fairlea. As long as he was doing something to and from work, he was able to drive."

"Are you aware there is no law that allows an employer to sign a temporary driver's permit for an employee to . . . ."

"I believe it's from the state of Ohio, where he had come from," she said.

"And you're saying it was valid in West Virginia?"

"I have no idea. I don't know anything about that."

"Do you recall telling Trooper Johnson, 'It was the morning of the 10th when we left the TEMAC office, at the same time. My son has to be at day care at 9:30, and it was the 10th.'?"

"I probably did say that."

"Why did you tell him that?"

"I couldn't tell you anything I said, on the night I saw . . . heard . . . those gun shots. Those guys told me Tod was still alive. Then they told me gruesome things they were going to do to him and to my family. I was trying to protect my family." All the time she was speaking this, her expression was as blank as a slate.

"Don't you think you could have protected them better if you had gone to the police and had them help you?"

"I did go to them. I called the police on the fifteenth and gave lots of evidence to show them what was going on."

"You gave them a thirty-five page statement on October 17th, 1990, at the Lewisburg state police office. Only you and Trooper Johnson were at the Lewisburg Detachment. Why didn't you tell him about your concerns then?"

"Because they were still threatening my family and always talking about this third person that was watching my children."

"Madam, we just established that you were alone with a state trooper at the state trooper's office."

"Where do you think my son was, when I was there with a state trooper? He was with Rachel Johnson because I wasn't allowed to take him."

"Are you saying Rachel Johnson was holding a gun on your son?"

"They threatened me with that."

"If Rachel Johnson was threatening your son, wouldn't the best thing to do be to have the police go with you and help your son out?"

"And have him shot? I told you, I didn't think very clearly that week."

"Well, if these people were threatening you — Harry Joe Johnson and Roger Cline — why is it they confessed and told the police the truth before you did?"

"Because you offered Harry a deal to testify against me. Harry told me."

"Ms. Wilson, Harry Joe Johnson testified from the witness stand that he first gave a statement at Mullican's Lumber. There was no deal offered to him. You called him before the police talked to him and told him the police were coming, didn't you?"

"I don't remember calling him."

"On October 11th, 1990, did you purchase, with a Visa card belonging to Tod McQuaid, a ticket for Curt Wilson to come to Greenbrier County, West Virginia?"

"Yes, I did," she said, her face still a complete blank. "Curt Wilson is my husband, and I told him to come and get my son out of here, that something was going on, and I didn't feel safe with him here. He came but didn't take my son back with him because he didn't want to."

"In your last statement to the police, which was after you were arrested, you indicated that the killing took place at your house, and that you were there, is that right?"

"Yes, but like I told you before, I never saw Tod dead."

"You made statements such as, 'The second it happened I was sorry.' 'I really didn't think Roger would do it.' 'I have sat down at the TEMAC office the last two weeks and ran it just like Tod would have wanted me to.' 'I think we were all just crazy.' 'How could we do this?' What did you mean by all of that?"

Tammy took a deep breath. As far away as I was from her, I

swear that I could hear her inhale. "I was sorry it happened, because Officer Johnson asked me how I felt about Tod. Wouldn't you be sorry if somebody you loved died? I don't remember the questions he asked me. I really didn't think Roger would do it. I called Tod's parents and told them somebody needed to get down here and take care of the business. I don't know anything about the alarm business. Nobody could run it but Tod."

"Why did you keep trying to push this over on Evelyn Gettman? Why did you say she is the one involved?"

"I believed she was, and I still believe she may have something to do with it."

"You sent the police to Meadow Bridge on an eight-hour investigation?"

"That's where they told me they put him. I didn't dream somebody would drive him all the way to Ohio."

"You heard them say, 'You wanted him out of the state.' You didn't say that?"

"No, I did not."

Rick walked a little closer to her, as if he were stalking her. "Why did you tell Mrs. McQuaid in your conversation with her on or about October 15th that Tod asked you to marry him and that Tod was the father of your son?"

"Mrs. McQuaid may have been mistaken in what I said in our three conversations. I remember telling her I thought I was pregnant."

(Despite all the lies she had told, I still couldn't get over the gall of this woman. I remembered exactly what she had said over the phone; in fact, her words kept playing in my mind every night, keeping me awake.)

"Do you remember inviting Mrs. McQuaid or talking about them coming down for Thanksgiving in your October 15th conversation?" Rick asked.

"Not on the 15th, no."

"Are you saying that Mrs. McQuaid is wrong about the date?"

"She would have to be because me and Tod both talked this over with her in person when we visited them in New York."

"Ms. Wilson, why didn't you go get medical attention for Tod or call the police immediately after this incident?" Rick Lorensen said, his voice loud and insistent.

"Because they told me the other person ...." Tammy paused, then began again, more slowly. "Because Harry didn't leave me alone but for thirty minutes the next day."

"Why didn't you go to the police then?"

"Do you know what I was like in the morning? How would you feel if somebody was shot in your house, somebody that you had just made love to, that you really cared about?"

(Somebody you cared for so much that you didn't even think of getting help for him. Right.)

Rick seemed to be reading my mind, or perhaps I had read his. "You didn't care enough about him to call the police and say that something was wrong."

Tammy shifted her weight on the chair. "They told me he was alive and they would kill him if I called anybody. These people came into my house and shot the person I was in love with, and you want me not to take somebody like that seriously? They went to my son's preschool one day and picked him up without me knowing it, and when I called to get him, he was gone."

Rick turned his face from her for a moment and appeared to be thinking hard. "The one thing I don't understand about all of this, Ms. Wilson, is, if you were so fearful of them, why did they turn themselves in first?"

Tammy didn't pause a beat. "Because they started playing games with each other. Harry thought Roger was going to shoot him and vice versa. They would take guns out at night and point them at each other."

"Roger turned himself in, right?"

"Yes, he did."

"And Harry Joe Johnson gave a statement and turned himself in?"

"Yes, he did."

"I have no further questions, your Honor."

Mr. Hunter stood up and approached his client. "One matter, your honor," he said, then addressed Tammy and showed her some papers. "On this document, page 2 of exhibit 50, there's some handwriting. Whose is it?"

"It's Tod's."

"These are your application forms and notes that Tod McQuaid took during your interview. Have you ever seen this document before?"

"He would never let me look through my file, although I always wondered what he thought of me on that first interview," Tammy said.

(In reality, Tammy's application and other documents were in the file cabinet along with those of all the other TEMAC employees, which she could access any time.)

"This writing says, 'Has strong motivation, sensible, and a personable character. Highly military qualified,'" Mr. Hunter said. "'Attractive looking, well spoken, and intelligent.' Is that what you wrote on that document, or what Tod wrote?"

"It got Tod's signature on it, doesn't it?"

Tammy was excused from the witness stand.

I wondered how Steve Hunter knew what personal information Tod had written on Tammy Wilson's TEMAC application, especially when it was still in the TEMAC office file cabinet. Did he, in fact, go through the file in the TEMAC office? Another unanswered question. There was, however, one important thing he forgot to read to the jurors, and I think he omitted it on purpose. In big bold letters on the side of Tammy's application, Tod had written, *MAYBE!*

# CHAPTER EIGHTEEN

I left the courtroom feeling as if I had fallen off a precipice. When Rog appeared and took my hand, I thanked Tyler — who had kindly stayed with me — and all but fell into Rog's arms. "There's only so much evil I can listen to at one time," I explained, when we were well out of the courthouse. "That woman can lie the whiskers off a rat!"

That night, in the motel, Rog read Bob's notes and agreed with my assessment. "First she says that she made two phone calls to us, then says that it was three," he said with a sigh. "Of course, compared to the real whoppers in her testimony, I guess that's just a little fib. Well, soon it will be all over. Tomorrow the summations will be given, and once the verdict is in, that's the end."

I said nothing. Yes, it would be over, but in a sense, this ordeal would never really be over, we'd never really reach an end. I'd never hear Tod say, "You're the best, Mom." We would never again enjoy hearing him recite the entire dialogue of *Star Wars,* complete with the sound effects — Ka-thunk! Ooeeooo! Wwwwzippp! — that made us all laugh. We would never have him with us as we shared in the excitement of family gatherings. No, our feelings of loss would never end.

The phone rang, and Jan jumped to answer it. Finally, the call she'd been waiting for so long had come. It was Mike, announcing the birth of his daughter, their new granddaughter. We shared in their joy. The rest of the evening, Jan's mind was focused on Baby Kayleigh and the prospect of being able to see and hold her.

I began watching TV in bed to help me forget about the

upcoming verdict. Would the jury see her as I did, a heartless murderer, or would they buy her absurd stories? I didn't remember falling asleep, but suddenly Rog was whispering in my ear, "Time to get up, hon." I awoke with a start, confused at first, then astounded. I had slept through the night, free of nightmares, for the first time in over a week. I couldn't help but ask myself as I took my shower and got dressed, could this be an omen?

It was time to hear the final arguments in the case. We entered the courtroom and took a seat in the front row, and I felt relieved that I no longer had to hide my face. I looked around to see who might have come in and noticed that the man and boy who had sat in the hall the day before were now sitting in the last row, not far from where I had been sitting. None of Tammy Wilson's family were present. Perhaps they didn't care enough to want to know her fate.

Rick Lorensen and Steve Hunter walked in, took their places and simultaneously opened their briefcases, shuffling papers while they prepared for their closing arguments. As the bailiff escorted Tammy to the defense table, she walked with an air of confidence, her head high and her back straight. She looked more like an executive attending a stockholder meeting than a woman with her life on the line. Tammy sat down and looked around intently, as if to check out who was in attendance. I couldn't help but wonder what was going on in her mind on this day. Although I couldn't account for it very well, I personally had the feeling that she truly thought that she had done no wrong. Tammy gave a faint smile as she looked toward the back of the room. It was meant for the man and boy, and it was obvious she knew them.

The defense had prepared her well for this final day. She was dressed in a prim, navy blue print dress with a white collar. Her hair was pulled back neatly and she wore very little makeup, just a hint of pink lipstick. Then I noticed her "prop" leaning against the leg of her chair, facing the jury box. A Bible. I almost laughed out loud at the irony of this, and I couldn't help but wonder whose idea that was.

I glanced up as someone sat down beside me. It was our Jeff. Seeing him made me light up. He had driven all the way from Pittsburgh to be with us on this crucial day. He reached over and gripped my hand. "How are you doing, Mom?"

"I'm fine … now," I said, as I squeezed his long, strong fingers. I looked up at him, beaming, and thanked God I still had him!

The bailiff escorted the jurors in at 9:00 A.M. while Judge Jolliffe took his place at the bench, calling court to order. He glanced around as if he, too, wanted to see who was present.

Rick rose and addressed the jury first. "When I first stood up and spoke to you on Monday morning, I asked you to consider three things after I gave a brief summary of what evidence and type of evidence you would hear. I asked you to consider the sanctity of life, Tod McQuaid's life, the life of the eldest son of the McQuaids. I asked you to consider the sanctity of trust, the trust we have in one another as fellow human beings to act morally and responsibly. And I asked you to consider the sanctity of truth, that is, to come forward and say what happened in a manner that lets the chips fall where they may, to say what happened so people will know what has happened, so the McQuaids might know what has happened to their son."

He left his table and walked slowly, somberly over to the jury box, facing the twelve solemn jurors as he continued. He spoke of the witnesses as they appeared on the stand and reiterated their testimony. Harry Joe Johnson, tired of the lies. The offer Tammy made, the meeting to plan Tod's murder. Tammy calling Harry Joe Johnson to warn him that the police were on their way. It was Harry Joe's statement that broke the case for Sergeants Johnson and Sloan. Next was my testimony. The conversations Tammy Wilson and I had had, telling me Evelyn Gettman had threatened to kill Tod, and later, that Tod was having a heart attack. How he wanted to buy her a ring and marry her and how she claimed that Tod was her son's father. All this after Tod had been dead for over a week.

Rick reminded the jury about Roger Cline stating how Tammy wanted him to shoot her ex-husband and having Roger clean out all the Broncos the day before he was arrested. What did he have to gain by his testimony? He had already said that he shot Tod. And of course Rick told them about Tammy Wilson taking the stand. He pointed out the fact that Tammy Wilson didn't break down and cry or shed one tear when they talked about the remains of Tod, and how she kept her composure throughout the trial. She claimed Roger

Cline was the mastermind behind the whole thing, and that the man she loved was killed in her home. Harry Joe Johnson was to have held her down the whole time so that she couldn't run for help. Harry Joe had blood on him while holding her down, but Harry Joe was also going outside to get Roger Cline to come back and finish the job. Harry Joe Johnson said he committed murder. Tammy Wilson says she did absolutely nothing wrong.

Rick ended his summation with these remarks: "Mr. and Mrs. McQuaid have one son now, Jeff, who is sitting with them today." He looked over at us, pointing to Jeff. "They had another good-looking boy. Everyone that has talked about him liked him. There was a lot of evidence about him wanting to help people when they needed some help. They had a boy with a successful business. He had two young children, and now he is gone. Tammy Wilson gave the police four different statements, she said. Only yesterday did she tell the truth. I think she came as close to telling the truth as she ever came in the State's Exhibit No. 21, when she said, 'It was my fault. The second it happened I was sorry. It's my fault, and I punished them for helping me. I really didn't think Roger would do it.' That indicates there was a plan beforehand. Please, on behalf of the McQuaids, find the truth about their son. Their son left unburied, to rot away in another state, unknown to them. Now that it's come out, what has happened? Tod McQuaid was somebody's son, somebody's father, somebody's brother. We can give him and those who loved him peace by returning the truth. Not the lies that Tammy Wilson would have you believe, but the truth in his case."

Rick returned to his table and sat down. I dabbed my eyes with a tissue, genuinely moved by his words. I looked at Tammy, but her face was still maddeningly blank, minus all emotion. She sat like a rock, no expression, no life, no heart, no soul. Judge Jolliffe called a ten minute recess, which I welcomed.

In the hallway, I noticed Sergeant Johnson speaking to the man and boy, and when he finished, I went up to him and asked who they were. "All the older man said was, 'A friend of Tammy's,' " Sergeant Johnson replied. "That doesn't say much, does it?"

When we returned to the courtroom, it was Mr. Hunter's turn to address the jury. He left his table, walked to the witness chair, sat down, looked at the jury and began speaking. "I grew up on a farm in Greenbrier County. Probably Trooper Johnson and I are the only two guys here that talk with more of a Southern lingo than anybody else."

Mr. Hunter decided to give his summation using the good-old-boy approach. The only thing missing was a straw hat and a stalk of hay in the corner of his mouth. He talked about his life on the farm before television, when the big excitement of the day was the mail delivery. He loved listening to his grandfather sitting in his rocking chair on the front porch, reading the letters he received. With that, he took the piece of paper he held in his hand and began reading:

"Dear folks, it seems like we have been apart several days since I last talked with you at the selection of the jury and in my opening statements. Folks, the name of this case is: The State of West Virginia vs. Tammy S. Wilson. What a formidable name. What a strong opponent. As Judge Jolliffe told you, the indictment is only an accusation against Tammy, and is not any evidence of her guilt. It's simply finger-pointing. You are the people who promised in the jury selection process that you would not convict on speculation. The state provided a deal for Harry Joe Johnson. You remember that his wife contradicted a great deal of this testimony, but she was truthful about certain things that he was not. Roger Cline was the man who admitted he killed Tod McQuaid. What did those three state witnesses prove beyond a reasonable doubt against Tammy Wilson? Tammy Wilson is a person like me. Tammy Wilson will hurt if she is convicted unjustly. I ask only that you treat her fairly.

"You know, if we were outside the courtroom, and sitting in your living room or mine, on our couches, around the fire, a beer in your hand, we wouldn't have any trouble at all with this case. Tammy Wilson did not have to take the stand, but she did in order to declare her innocence. Had she been permitted to do so, she would have screamed it from the rooftops, because she is innocent. We know you are going to live up to your role. You will remember this case every day of your life. So as you go to your homes and put out the light, your conscience will be clear, for you will have found Tammy Wilson not guilty. I say to you, your verdict must be, " 'Not guilty.' "

How I wanted to stand up and shout, "Yes, Mr. Hunter, we will remember this case every day of our lives," and at last, that is an honest-to-God, truthful statement.

Judge Jolliffe addressed the jurors. Since it was close to noon, he dismissed the court for lunch before deliberation began.

Rog, Jeff, Bob, Jan, and I went to a Greek restaurant we had enjoyed earlier in the week. Since we knew it would be a while before the jury would be back in the courtroom, we didn't feel compelled to hurry. At one point in the meal, Jeff asked me if I was okay, and I told him that I was fine.

"Just checking," he said, grinning widely. "I have to keep you here at the table, or else you're like to blast out of your chair at any minute and take off for the courthouse like a misguided missile."

"I'm sorry I'm so fidgety," I said, as I twisted my linen napkin around my fingers. "I just can't help thinking about the trial and the jurors and . . . ."

Jeff patted my hand and kissed my cheek. "Mom, come on, forget about all that for a little while. Relax. Take it easy." Jeff began telling me little stories to make me laugh, anecdotes about the girls and tales of long-ago adventures with Tod. His boundless sense of humor always brings joy, and today was no different. It meant a lot to me to have him with us.

At 1:30 we arrived back at the courthouse and found the courtroom empty. We sat down and the long, long wait began. Little by little, people trickled back. Rick walked over to us. "You folks doing okay?" he asked.

"What ... what if the jury comes back with a verdict of guilty with mercy?" I asked, unable to hide my fear. "Tammy could be out in ten years or less."

Rick gave me the oddest, smallest shadow of a smile. "I don't think we have to worry. I think we have her right where we want her." He raised his hand slightly and clenched it into a fist. "Keep the faith, Jan."

At 4:25 P.M. Judge Jolliffe took his place behind the bench as the bailiff announced that the jurors were ready to return. Silence overwhelmed the courtroom like a storm cloud. I watched the jurors take their seats, then stared one last time at my son's killer. I wanted to see the reaction on her face when the verdict was read. She sat beside

Steve Hunter, motionless and emotionless. For one fleeting moment, I wondered if she really cared what the outcome would be.

Judge Jolliffe addressed the jury. "Ladies and gentlemen, I am going to read the verdict as signed by your foreman. I would ask each of you to listen carefully. I will be inquiring as to whether or not it is, in fact, your verdict." The judge cleared his throat, then read from the paper in front of him. "State of West Virginia versus Tammy S. Wilson — We the jury find the defendant, Tammy S. Wilson, guilty of murder in the first degree of Tod McQuaid. We the jury find that the defendant, Tammy S. Wilson, did commit the crime of murder in the first degree as charged in the indictment, with the use of presentment or brandishing of a firearm, and is guilty of murder in the first degree without mercy."

A strange sensation that felt a little like joy made me gasp for breath. The bitch had lost! I grabbed Rog and Jeff's hands and clutched them hard. "Thank God!" I murmured. "Justice has been done."

"Ladies and gentlemen, you have heard the verdict as read and reported by your foreman," Judge Jolliffe said again. "Is there any member of the jury who dissents or disagrees with the verdict as read and returned?"

At that moment I held my breath and quickly prayed no one would answer. There was dead silence. *Thank You, God,* I said silently. *Thank you thank you thank you!*

The judge addressed Tammy and pronounced her prison sentence, ending with a solemn promise. "You will be in prison until the day you die." As harsh as those words might have seemed to others, they were among the sweetest I had ever heard.

Although I watched her face carefully all that time, I can honestly say that Tammy Wilson's expression never changed, not one iota. She shed no tears and certainly showed no remorse. I'm not sure she was even listening to what the judge was saying, or that she cared, for that matter. I was satisfied that someone so evil, so unredeemable would never walk the public streets again.

Rick Lorensen approached us and we shook his hand and expressed our gratitude. I glanced over at Tammy, who was now inexplicably cheerful and fully engaged in a discussion with the bailiff. She gestured to the man and boy who were still in the back of the courtroom, holding up five fingers. It was her way of telling them that they could visit her at five o'clock. She had to have known they would be in the courtroom that day. I was appalled that she was more interested in these two people visiting her than the fact that she was going to prison for the rest of her life. Did she think she could still somehow weasel her way out of the sentence, or perhaps appeal the case and overturn it? Who knows what her diseased mind was thinking? I hoped that Tammy heard those four gun shots every day as long as she breathed.

Tammy Wilson was sentenced to life in prison, without parole. The trial was over, but for our family, the ordeal would never be over. Someone we loved would always be missing from our lives. Tammy Wilson had ripped him from us with a cruelty that was hard to imagine, let alone believe. But it was true, and that was the only consolation we had received: the truth, and the justice that went along with it.

# CHAPTER NINETEEN

Even after the trial, I still couldn't bring myself to fully accept Tod's death. Somehow, I knew I had to prepare for the busy weeks ahead, even though I was exhausted, physically and mentally. I began to have mixed emotions about moving and leaving the home our boys grew up in and all our friends of twenty-seven years. Did we really need this much change, especially so soon after the trial? Maybe. Rog felt that being close to family might help with my depression, which certainly didn't seem to be getting any better.

I continued having recurring violent dreams at night and would awaken in a cold sweat, my heart beating like a metronome. I would get out of bed and pace quietly around the house or go into the family room and sit in front of the sliding glass doors, looking out into the darkness at the stars glittering in the sky. As I watched the stars, I would whisper, "Are you up there, Tod? Are you watching over us? I hope you know how much I love you and miss you." Many nights I would sit at the doors long enough to watch the stars disappear and the sun rise.

Finally, moving day arrived. Once the house was empty, I quietly walked around, looking at the rooms, each of which held many dozens of wonderful memories. Tod and Jeff's rooms had long ago lost the masculine look they had once sported and had been overwhelmed with frills and lace once the girls took over. Tod's room, like Tod, had always been full of surprises. Once, while Rog and I were away for a weekend, he had painted his room light blue with a huge yellow sun at one end of the ceiling and sunbeams reaching across the entire ceiling. He was so proud of his artwork, and I had to admit it was impressive. When Heather moved into the room, that splendid, sunny ceiling had been repainted with a darker blue and dotted with stars that glowed in the dark.

I then wandered down to the end of the hall to the bedroom that had once been ours, then Rose's. As I stood in the middle of the room, looking all around, sadness began to take over me. I stared at the doorframe leading into the dressing room area. It hadn't been painted in twenty-seven years because it was more than a doorframe: It was also the pencil-marked growth chart of Tod and Jeff. I remembered all the laughter and fun we had had as we measured the boys while they stood against the frames in their shoes, then without shoes. They stood straight, trying to stretch an inch or two taller than they really were. What a proud moment when they finally could brag they were taller than Mom!

I sat down on the floor staring at the growth chart, recalling what my mother wrote in one of my autograph books as a teenager. At the time I didn't understand it, but as I thought of all the happy times in our home, I understood what she had meant. "Cherish all your memories. They make a fine cushion for old age." I sat there lost in memories and had the distinct feeling that Tod was with me.

We settled into our new home without trouble or fanfare, and my days continued to be up and down. I missed not being able to call Tod. So many times I would go to the phone out of habit, only to realize that he wasn't there, I couldn't reach him. There wasn't a day that passed that I didn't think of him. When the phone rang, how I wanted it to be him, though I knew it wasn't. People began telling me that I had to let him go, that I would never find peace within as long as I held on. How easy it was for them to give me that advice when they hadn't been through such an ordeal. It simply isn't that easy to let go, partly because your child is never gone, even if he's dead. He's always with you, inside you.

My nightmares followed me to the new house, and every night I prayed for help to put my mind at ease and extinguish my disturbing dreams for good. Then one night I had a different kind of dream. We were having a party in our new home with all our neighbors. I was standing in the doorway of the kitchen facing the hallway when the front door opened. As I glanced down the hall to see who was coming in, there stood Tod, wearing the blue plaid shirt and blue jeans I had given him on our last Christmas together. I was so excited seeing him, but for some reason I couldn't get close to him. He never moved away from the front door, just stood inside of it holding it open. "Oh, Tod, I'm so glad you found us," I said. "I wanted to tell you that they're trying to kill you."

He looked at me wearily. "I know," he said. And with that, he turned, and the door closed. I opened the door and stood calling for him to come back, but he was gone.

Rog gently shook me. I had been shouting in my sleep. When I awoke, I realized I had been dreaming. I felt so disappointed! I hadn't seen Tod after all. I lay back thinking about that dream, wondering what it could have meant. Was there any truth in it?

A few nights later, I dreamed that Tod and I were walking together along a sunlit, wooded path. He was wearing the same blue plaid shirt and jeans. I had no idea where we were going or where we were coming from. Tod was chatting away as he used to do, and we were laughing and chatting together, although I couldn't remember specifically what Tod was saying. I did know, however, that we were happy and having a good time being together. I actually woke myself up laughing. Again I had to wonder, what could this dream mean? I wanted to believe that Tod was telling me he was happy and content.

A few nights later I had my final dream of Tod. We were walking on the same path again, but it was twilight and getting dark fast. Tod was still dressed in the same shirt and jeans. He had his arm around my shoulder in a loving, protective embrace. I was talking to him, explaining to him how I wanted to turn the clock back for a little while so we could spend more time together. He turned to look at me with a serious expression and said, "Mom, I'm sorry, but we can't do that."

"Please, Tod, just for a little while," I kept saying to him.

"Mom, we can never go back," he replied. "You must go on alone now." I began crying and begging, but he was firm. "We can never go back. You must go on." With that, dark shadows of night washed over him, and he was gone.

I woke myself up crying. I quietly climbed out of bed and went to the first floor where I sat in Rog's recliner and continued to weep for a long time. The dream was real. Tod was real. I sat in the darkness, reliving that dream. Was this God's way of telling me to let go? For some reason I felt compelled to read my Bible. I opened it, and as I leafed through it, I came upon, the passage commonly known as, *"The Immoral Woman."* I read it like a drowning person grasping at a life preserver.

*Suddenly he was going with her like an ox on the way to be slaughtered, like a deer prancing into a trap, where an arrow would pierce its heart. He was like a bird going into a net, he did not know his life was in danger. Now then sons, listen to me, pay attention to what I say. Do not let such a woman win your heart: Don't go wandering after her. She has been the ruin of many men and caused death to too many to count. If you should go into her house, you are on the way to the world of the dead. It's a shortcut to death.*

I read that passage over and over and decided it was God's way of telling me exactly what had happened to our Tod.

I confess I sometimes imagine Tammy in a small, dark cell, bored to tears and despised by almost everyone, without pretty clothes or makeup or the freedom to take a walk in the sunlight on a woodland path or listen to the cardinals singing in the spring. It's not a very big price to pay for my son's life, but it will do.

There will always be reminders of Tod that will trigger my grief and tears for many years to come. He will never leave my heart. I have thirty-five years of wonderful memories and home movies to remember him by. Memories fade, however, and movies don't allow me to put my arms around Tod and hug him.

I continue to stargaze on clear bright nights, and when I see a brilliant, sparkling star, I know in my heart that Tod is watching over us. Even when the nights are cloudy, I know there's a star glittering up there just for me and my family. I look up at the heavens and softly whisper, "Remember, Tod, I love you." If I close my eyes and relax completely, I can sometimes hear the gentle echo of his voice in reply: "You're the best, Mom."

# LIFE GOES ON

*Time can heal the worst of wounds,*
*As it has with mine.*
*But along with healing, I tend to forget*
*The details I once comprised.*
*An evil woman — no heart, no soul —*
*Took your life away.*
*Two little girls, fatherless, left*
*On Earth without you remain.*
*You were so young, only thirty-five,*
*And had much more life to live.*
*You were supposed to be there for my childhood,*
*Watch me grow,*
*Give all the love you had to give.*
*I must accept life as is, which I have done so far.*
*Give me away for my wedding, sadly, you will not,*
*But watch quietly from your star.*
*Please do not forget me, Dad,*
*Or think that I've forgotten you.*
*I swear to you with all my heart*
*That my love is eternal and true.*

— Elizabeth Anna McQuaid, Age 17

# WHERE ARE THEY NOW?

Harry Joe Johnson plea-bargained and testified against Tammy Wilson and Roger Cline. He was released from the Denmar Correctional Center, Hillsboro, West Virginia on October 25, 1999, after serving nine years of his eighteen-year prison term.

Roger Cline was sentenced to a term of ten years to life with mercy. On October 12, 2000, Cline met before the West Virginia parole board at the St. Mary's Correctional Center, St. Mary's West Virginia, and was denied parole. He applied to the governor of the state of West Virginia requesting executive clemency. In July 2001, he was denied. On October 8, 2003, Roger Cline appeared before the parole board and was again denied parole.

Tammy Wilson is serving a life sentence at the Pruntytown Correctional Center, Pruntytown, West Virginia, never to be paroled.